2B

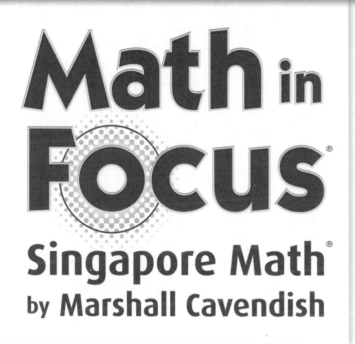

Math in Focus

Singapore Math®
by Marshall Cavendish

Reteach

Consultant and Author
Dr. Fong Ho Kheong

Author
Ang Kok Cheng

Marshall Cavendish
Education

U.S. Distributor

**Houghton
Mifflin
Harcourt**

© 2015 Marshall Cavendish Education Private Limited

Published by Marshall Cavendish Education
An imprint of Marshall Cavendish Education Private Limited
Times Centre, 1 New Industrial Road, Singapore 536196
Customer Service Hotline: (65) 6213 9444
U.S. Office Tel: (1-914) 332 8888 Fax: (1-914) 332 8882
E-mail: tmesales@mceducation.com
Website: www.mceducation.com

Distributed by
Houghton Mifflin Harcourt
222 Berkeley Street
Boston, MA 02116
Tel: 617-351-5000
Website: www.hmheducation.com/mathinfocus

First published 2015

Math in Focus® Reteach 2B
ISBN 978-0-544-19250-8

Printed in Singapore

1 2 3 4 5 6 7 8   1401   20 19 18 17 16 15
4500463652   A B C D E

Contents

CHAPTER 13 Customary Measurement of Length

CHAPTER 14 Time

CHAPTER 15 Multiplication Tables of 3 and 4

Introducing

Math in Focus®

Reteach

Reteach 2A and *2B*, written to complement *Math in Focus®: Singapore Math®* by Marshall Cavendish Grade 2, offer a second opportunity to practice skills and concepts at the entry level. Key vocabulary terms are explained in context, complemented by sample problems with clearly worked solutions.

Not all children are able to master a new concept or skill after the first practice. A second opportunity to practice at the same level before moving on can be key to long-term success.

Monitor students' levels of understanding during daily instruction and as they work on Practice exercises. Provide *Reteach* worksheets to struggling students who would benefit from further practice at a basic level.

CHAPTER 10 Mental Math and Estimation

Worksheet 1   Meaning of Sum

Circle the sum.

┌─ **Example** ───────────────────────────────────┐

$32 + 44 = \boxed{76}$

The **sum** is the whole or total when two or more numbers are added together.

└──┘

1. $23 + 54 = 77$

2. $293 = 225 + 68$

3. $145 + 123 = 268$

4. $1,000 = 823 + 177$

Find the sum of the numbers.
Use bar models to help you.

5.

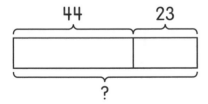

$44 + 23 = $ _____

6.

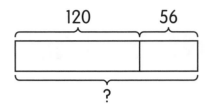

120 + 56 = _____

Solve.
Use bar models to help you.

7.   Letitia has 234 stickers.
Sheila has 425 stickers.
Find the sum of the number of stickers they have.

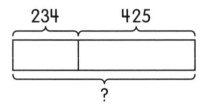

The sum is _____.

Solve.
Draw bar models to help you.

8.   Roland has 178 building blocks.
Perla has 258 building blocks.
Find the sum of the number of building blocks they have.

The sum is _____.

Worksheet 2   Mental Addition

Add mentally.
Use number bonds to help you.

1.   Find 17 + 2.
Group 17 into tens and ones.

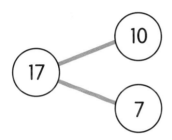

Step 1   Add the ones.   7 + 2 = _____

Step 2   Add the result to   10 + _____ = _____
the tens.

So, 17 + 2 = _____.

2.   12 + 3 = _____

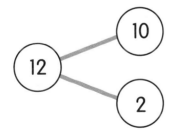

Add mentally.
Use number bonds to help you.

Example

Find 77 + 6.

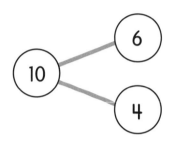

Adding 6 is the same as adding 10 and subtracting 4.

Step 1 Add 10 to 77. $77 + 10 = \underline{87}$

Step 2 Subtract 4 from the $\underline{87} - \underline{4} = \underline{83}$
result.

So, 77 + 6 = $\underline{83}$.

---

3.   Find 56 + 9.

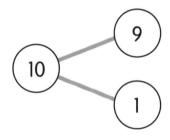

Step 1 Add 10 to 56.   _____ + 10 = _____

Step 2 Subtract 1 from the   _____ − _____ = _____
result.

So, 56 + 9 = _____.

Name: _____ **Date:** _____

Add mentally.
Use number bonds to help you.

> ### Example
>
> Find 156 + 3.
>
> Group 156 into ones, and hundreds and tens.
>
>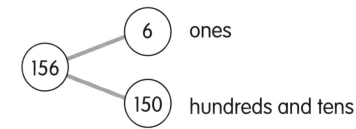
>
> **Step 1** Add the ones. $\underline{\quad 6 \quad} + 3 = \underline{\quad 9 \quad}$
>
> **Step 2** Add the result to the $150 + \underline{\quad 9 \quad} = \underline{159}$
>   hundreds and tens.
>
> So, 156 + 3 = $\underline{159}$.

4. Find 143 + 4.

Group 143 into ones, and hundreds and tens.

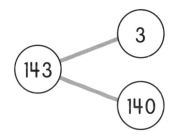

Step 1 Add the ones. $\underline{\qquad} + 4 = \underline{\qquad}$

Step 2 Add the result to the $140 + \underline{\qquad} = \underline{\qquad}$
           hundreds and tens.

So, 143 + 4 = $\underline{\qquad}$.

Add mentally.
Use number bonds to help you.

┌─ **Example** ───┐

Find 147 + 6.

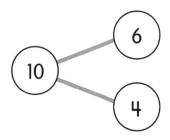

Adding 6 is the same as adding 10 and subtracting 4.

Step 1   Add 10 to 147.

Step 2   Subtract 4 from the result.

$147 + 10 = \underline{\mathit{157}}$

$\underline{\mathit{157}} - \underline{\mathit{4}} = \underline{153}$

So, $147 + 6 = \underline{\mathit{153}}$.

└───┘

5.   Find 256 + 7.

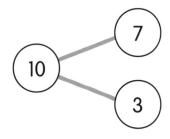

Step 1   Add 10 to 256.

Step 2   Subtract 3 from the result.

So, $256 + 7 = \underline{\quad}$.

$256 + 10 = \underline{\quad}$

$\underline{\quad} - 3 = \underline{\quad}$

Add mentally.
Use number bonds to help you.

6. Find 11 + 10.
Group 11 into tens and ones.

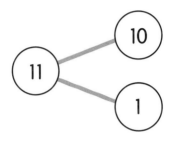

Step 1 Add the tens.   10 + 10 = _____

Step 2 Add the result to   _____ + _____ = _____
the ones.

So, 11 + 10 = _____.

7. 16 + 10 = _____

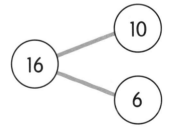

Add mentally.
Use number bonds to help you.

Example

Find 117 + 40.

Group 117 into tens, and hundreds and ones.

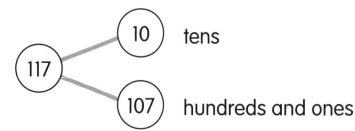

117 — 10 tens

107 hundreds and ones

Step 1   Add the tens. $40 + 10 = \underline{50}$

Step 2   Add the result to the $\underline{107} + \underline{50} = \underline{157}$
hundreds and ones.

So, 117 + 40 = $\underline{157}$.

---

8.   Find 334 + 20.

Group 324 into tens, and hundreds and ones.

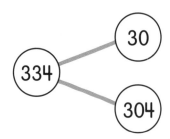

334 — 30

304

Step 1   Add the tens. $20 + 30 = \underline{\quad\quad}$

Step 2   Add the result to the $\underline{\quad\quad} + \underline{\quad\quad} = \underline{\quad\quad}$
hundreds and ones.

So, 334 + 20 = $\underline{\quad\quad}$.

Add mentally.
Use number bonds to help you.

┌─ **Example** ───┐

Find 328 + 90.

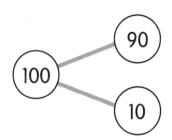

Adding 90 is the same as adding 100 and subtracting 10.

Step 1 Add 100 to 328.

Step 2 Subtract 10 from the result

$328 + 100 = \underline{428}$

$\underline{428} - \underline{10} = \underline{418}$

So, $328 + 90 = \underline{418}$.

└──┘

9. Find 232 + 60.

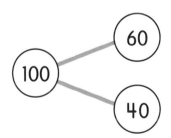

Step 1 Add 100 to 232.

$232 + 100 = \underline{}$

Step 2 Subtract 40 from the result.

$\underline{} - \underline{} = \underline{}$

So, $232 + 60 = \underline{}$.

Add mentally.
Use number bonds to help you.

Example

Find 128 + 300.

Group 128 into hundreds, and tens and ones.

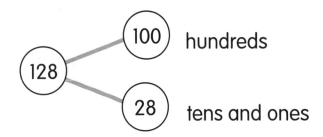

128 → 100 hundreds

128 → 28 tens and ones

Step 1   Add the hundreds.   _100_ + 300 = _400_

Step 2   Add the results to   _400_ + 28 = _428_
             the tens and ones.

So, 128 + 300 = _428_.

---

10.   Find 271 + 200.

Group 271 into hundreds, and tens and ones.

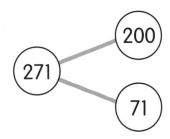

271 → 200

271 → 71

Step 1   Add the hundreds.   _____ + 200 = _____

Step 2   Add the results to the   _____ + 71 = _____
             tens and ones.

So, 271 + 200 = _____.

Worksheet 3 Meaning of Difference

Circle the difference.

Example

$98 - 54 = \boxed{44}$

To find the **difference**, subtract the number that is less from the number that is greater.

1. $85 = 153 - 68$

2. $256 - 103 = 153$

3. $586 = 700 - 114$

4. $403 - 199 = 204$

Find the difference between the numbers.
Use bar models to help you.

5.

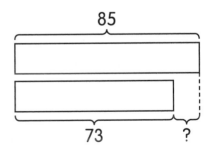

$85 - 73 =$ _____

6.

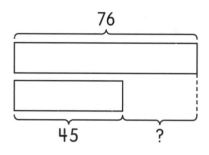

$$76 - 45 = \underline{\hspace{2cm}}$$

Solve.
Use bar models to help you.

7.   Leila has 34 apples.
Blake has 57 apples.
Find the difference between the numbers of apples.

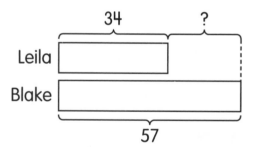

The difference is _____.

Solve.
Draw bar models to help you.

8.   Aidan made 99 paper frogs.
Beatrice made 44 paper frogs.
Find the difference between the numbers of paper frogs.

The difference is _____.

Worksheet 4   Mental Subtraction

Subtract mentally.
Use number bonds to help you.

1. Find 37 – 6.

Group 37 into tens and ones.

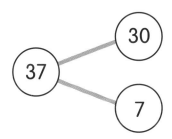

Step 1   Subtract the ones.   7 – 6 = _____

Step 2   Add the result to   30 + _____ = _____
the tens.

So, 37 – 6 = _____.

2. 29 – 4 = _____

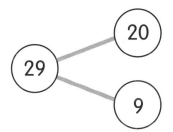

Subtract mentally.
Use number bonds to help you.

┌─ **Example** ───┐

Find 53 – 8.

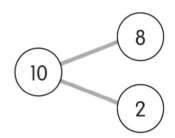

Subtracting 8 is the same as subtracting 10 and adding 2.

Step 1 Subtract 10 from 53. $53 - 10 = \underline{43}$

Step 2 Add 2 to the result. $\underline{43} + \underline{2} = \underline{45}$

So, 53 – 8 = $\underline{45}$.

└───┘

3.   Find 25 – 9.

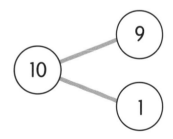

Step 1 Subtract 10 from 25. $25 - 10 = \underline{}$

Step 2 Add 1 to the result. $\underline{} + \underline{} = \underline{}$

So, 25 – 9 = $\underline{}$.

Subtract mentally.
Use number bonds to help you.

Example

Find 118 – 4.

Group 118 into ones, and hundreds and tens.

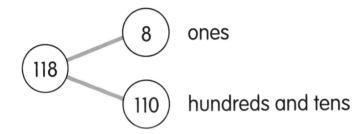

8 ones

118

110 hundreds and tens

Step 1 Subtract the ones.   8 – 4 = ___4___

Step 2 Add the result to the   ___110___ + ___4___ = ___114___
            hundreds and tens.

So, 118 – 4 = ___114___.

---

4. Find 136 – 2.

Group 136 into ones, and hundreds and tens.

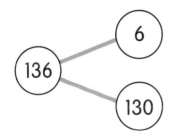

6

136

130

Step 1 Subtract the ones.   6 – 2 = _____

Step 2 Add the result to the   _____ + _____ = _____
            hundreds and tens.

So, 136 – 2 = _____.

Subtract mentally.
Use number bonds to help you.

┌─ **Example** ───┐

Find 232 – 7.

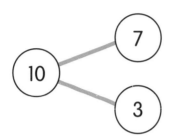

Subtracting 7 is the same as subtracting 10 and adding 3.

Step 1   Subtract 10 from 232. $232 - 10 = \underline{222}$

Step 2   Add 3 to the result. $\underline{222} + \underline{3} = \underline{225}$

So, 232 – 7 = $\underline{225}$.

└───┘

5.   Find 256 – 8.

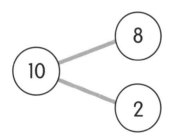

Step 1   Subtract 10 to 256. $256 - 10 = \underline{\hspace{1cm}}$

Step 2   Add 2 to the result. $\underline{\hspace{1cm}} + \underline{\hspace{1cm}} = \underline{\hspace{1cm}}$

So, 256 – 8 = $\underline{\hspace{1cm}}$.

Subtract mentally.
Use number bonds to help you.

6. Find 55 – 30.
Group 55 into tens and ones.

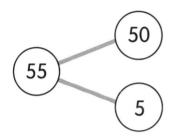

      Step 1 Subtract the tens.   50 – 30 = _____

      Step 2 Add the result to   5 + _____ = _____
                 the ones.

      So, 55 – 30 = _____.

7.   67 – 10 = _____

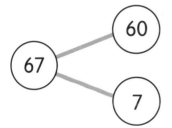

Subtract mentally.
Use number bonds to help you.

Example

Find 259 − 20.

Group 259 into tens, and hundreds and ones.

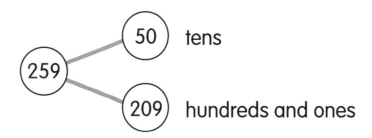

Step 1 Subtract the tens.   _50_ − 20 = _30_

Step 2 Add the result to the   209 + _30_ = _239_
hundreds and ones.

So, 259 − 20 = _239_.

---

8.   Find 142 − 30.

Group 142 into tens, and hundreds and ones.

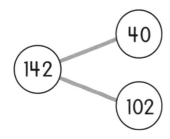

Step 1 Subtract the tens.   _____ − 30 = _____

Step 2 Add the result to the   102 + _____ = _____
hundreds and ones.

So, 142 − 30 = _____.

Subtract mentally.
Use number bonds to help you.

Example

Find 428 – 90.

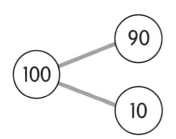

Subtracting 90 is the same as subtracting 100 and adding 10.

Step 1 Subtract 100 from 428. $428 - 100 = \underline{328}$

Step 2 Add 10 to the result. $\underline{328} + \underline{10} = \underline{338}$

So, 428 – 90 = $\underline{338}$.

---

9. Find 182 – 60.

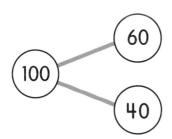

Step 1 Subtract 100 from 182.   _____ – _____ = _____

Step 2 Add 40 to the result.   _____ + _____ = _____

So, 182 – 60 = _____.

Subtract mentally.
Use number bonds to help you.

┌─ **Example** ───┐

Find 548 – 300.

Group 548 into hundreds, and tens and ones.

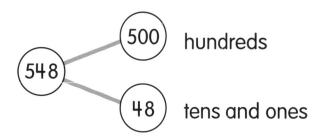

500 hundreds

548

48 tens and ones

Step 1 Subtract the hundreds. $\underline{500} - 300 = \underline{200}$

Step 2 Add the result to the $\underline{200} + 48 = \underline{248}$
tens and ones.

So, 548 – 300 = $\underline{248}$.

└───┘

10.   Find 428 – 200.

Group 428 into hundreds, and tens and ones.

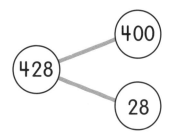

400

428

28

Step 1 Subtract the hundreds.   _____ – 200 = _____

Step 2 Add the result to the   _____ + 28 = _____
tens and ones.

So, 428 – 200 = _____.

Worksheet 5 Rounding Numbers to Estimate

Circle a group of 10 ○.
Estimate how many ○ there are.
Then count.

1.
○ ○ ○ ○ ○ ○ ○ ○ ○ ○ ○
○ ○ ○ ○ ○ ○ ○ ○ ○ ○ ○
○ ○ ○ ○ ○ ○ ○ ○ ○ ○ ○

When you **estimate** the number of an item, you find out about how many there are.

Estimate: _____

Count: _____

Find the missing numbers on the number line.

2.
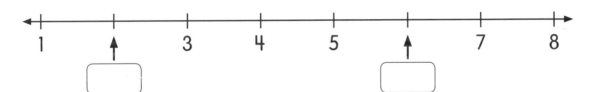

3.
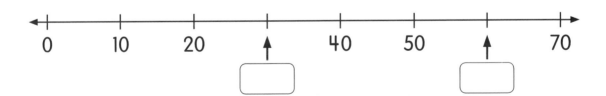

4.
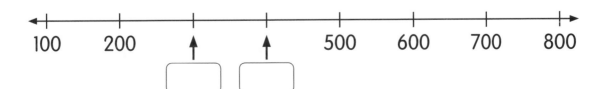

Mark each number with an X on the number line.
Round each number to the nearest ten and circle it.

┌─ **Example** ─────────────────────────────────┐

54

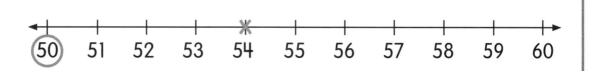

54 is about ___*50*___ when rounded to the nearest ten.

> Look at the digit in the ones place.
> If it is 1, 2, 3, or 4, round to the ten that is <u>less</u>.

└──┘

5.   31

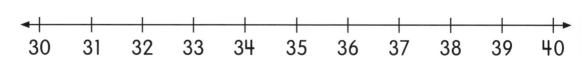

31 is about _____ when rounded to the nearest ten.

6.   72

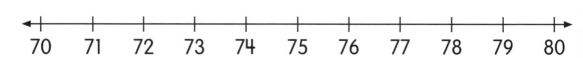

72 is about _____ when rounded to the nearest ten.

Mark each number with an X on the number line.
Round each number to the nearest ten and circle it.

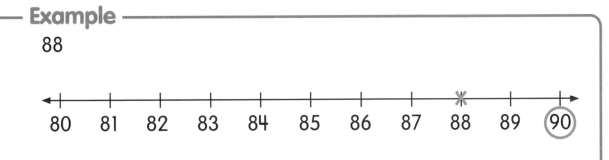

88 is about ____90____ when rounded to the nearest ten.

> Look at the digit in the ones place.
> If it is 5, 6, 7, 8, or 9, round to the <u>greater</u> ten.

7.   76

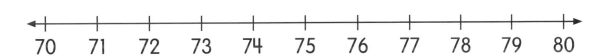

76 is about _____ when rounded to the nearest ten.

8.   49

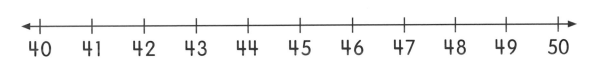

49 is about _____ when rounded to the nearest ten.

Mark each number with an X on the number line.
Round each number to the nearest ten and circle it.

─ Example ─

324

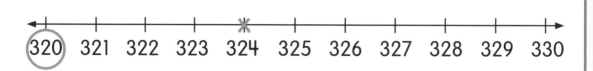

324 is about ___*320*___ when rounded to the nearest ten.

> Look at the digit in the ones place.
> If it is 1, 2, 3, or 4, round to the ten that is <u>less</u>.

9.   113

113 is about _____ when rounded to the nearest ten.

10.   661

661 is about _____ when rounded to the nearest ten.

Mark each number with an X on the number line.
Round each number to the nearest ten and circle it.

Example

258

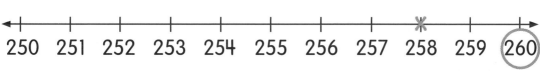

258 is about ___*260*___ when rounded to the nearest ten.

> Look at the digit in the ones place.
> If it is 5, 6, 7, 8, or 9, round to the <u>greater</u> ten.

11. 597

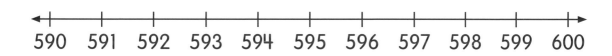

597 is about _____ when rounded to the nearest ten.

12. 915

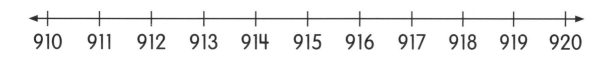

915 is about _____ when rounded to the nearest ten.

Find the missing numbers.

```
┌─ Example ──────────────────────────────────────────┐
│                                                     │
│     454 + 154 = 608                                 │
│                                      Estimate the sum│
│     454 is about ___450___.          of 454 and 154 │
│                                      to check if the│
│     154 is about ___150___.          answer is      │
│                                      reasonable.    │
│     454 + 154 is about ___600___.                   │
│                                                     │
│     Because ___600___ is close to 608,              │
│     the answer is reasonable.                       │
│                                                     │
└─────────────────────────────────────────────────────┘
```

13. 232 + 556 = 788

232 is about _____.

556 is about _____.

232 + 556 is about _____.

Because _____ is close to 788,
the answer is reasonable.

Add.
Use rounding to check that your answers are reasonable.

14. 158 + 265 = _____

Check: _____ + _____ = _____

15. 355 + 147 = _____

Check: _____ + _____ = _____

Find the missing numbers.

Example

355 – 142 = 213

355 is about ___*360*___.

142 is about ___*140*___.

355 – 142 is about ___*220*___.

Because ___*220*___ is close to 213,
the answer is reasonable.

> Estimate the difference between 355 and 142 to check if the answer is **reasonable**.

16.   439 – 127 = 312

439 is about _____.

127 is about _____.

439 – 127 is about _____.

Because _____ is close to 312,
the answer is reasonable.

Subtract.
Use rounding to check that your answers are reasonable.

17.   658 – 232 = _____

Check: _____ + _____ = _____

18.   529 – 214 = _____

Check: _____ + _____ = _____

Find the sum or difference.
Then round each number to the nearest ten.
Estimate the sum or difference to check that the answers are reasonable.

19.   152 + 89 = _____

152 is about _____.

89 is about _____.

152 + 89 is about _____ + _____.

Is the answer reasonable?

_____

20.   558 − 312 = _____

558 is about _____.

312 is about _____.

558 − 312 is about _____ − _____.

Is the answer reasonable?

_____

CHAPTER 11 Money

Worksheet 1   Coins and Bills

Write the value of each coin.

1.

_____ ¢

2.

_____ ¢

3.

_____ ¢

4.

_____ ¢

Circle the coins that make the given value.

5.   65¢

6.   80¢

Look at the bills.
Color the $1 bills blue, the $5 bills green, the $10 bills yellow, and the $20 bills red.

7.

Use your answers for Exercise 7.
How many are there?

8. _____ $1 bills

9. _____ $5 bills

10. _____ $10 bills

11. _____ $20 bills

Write the value of each bill.

Example

$_____1_____

12.

$_____

13.

$_____

Fill in the blanks.

Example

 =

1 ten-dollar bill   2 _*five-dollar*_ bills

14.

 =

1 twenty-dollar bill   2 _____ bills

Find the missing numbers.

┌─ **Example** ──┐

Suzi has some bills.
How much does Suzi have?
Count on from the greatest value.

$20 $40 $50

$55 $60 $61

$62 $63

20, 40, 50, 55, 60, 61, 62, 63 dollars.

Suzi has $___63___.

└──┘

15. Heather pays   for a book.

The book costs $_____.

16. Peter pays   for a sweater.

The sweater costs $_____.

Fill in the blanks.

— Example —

 =

1 one-dollar bill   4 ___quarters___

Count on in 25s.
25, 50, 75, 100.
$1 = 100¢

17.

 =

1 one-dollar bill   10 _____

Circle the coins that make one dollar.

18.

19.

Complete.
Write *less than, equal to,* or *more than.*

Example

25¢   →   35¢   →   40¢

40¢ is ___*less than*___ $1.

20.

25¢ → 50¢ → 60¢ → 70¢ → 80¢ → 90¢ → 100¢

100¢ is _____ $1.

21.

25¢   →   50¢   →   75¢   →   100¢   →   125¢

125¢ is _____ $1.

22.

25¢   →   35¢   →   40¢   →   41¢

41¢ is _____ $1.

Count the money.
How much money is there in all?

Example

Logan has a $1 bill, a quarter, and a penny.

$1		25¢		1¢
$1	→	$1.25	→	$1.26

Logan has ____*one*____ dollar and __*twenty-six*__ cents.

Logan has $ ____*1.26*____

> The decimal point helps you to see the number of cents and the number of dollars.

---

23. Hillary has a $5 bill, 2 dimes, and a nickel.

$5		10¢		10¢		5¢
$5	→	$5.10	→	$5.20	→	$5.25

Hillary has _____ dollars and _____ cents.

Hillary has $_____.

Count the money.
Then write the amount in two ways.

┌─ **Example** ─────────────────────────────────┐

Neve has a $5 bill and two $1 bills.

She has $_____*7*_____ or $____*7.00*____.

You can write two zeros after the decimal point when there are no cents.

└──┘

24. Ellie has a $10 bill and two $5 bills.

She has $_____ or $_____.

25. Dakota has a $20 bill and two $1 bills.

She has $_____ or $_____.

Count the money.
Then write the amount in two ways.

Example

Lucius has a quarter and 2 dimes.

He has ___45___ ¢ or $___0.45___.

You can write a zero before the decimal point when there are no dollars.

---

26. Todd has 3 dimes and a penny.

He has _____ ¢ or $_____.

27. Lucita has a quarter, 2 dimes, and a penny.

She has _____ ¢ or $_____.

Count the money.
Then write the amount in two ways.

Example

Annie has some money.

She has ____*15*____ dollars and ____*35*____ cents or $____*15.35*____.

Count on.
10 dollars, 15 dollars, 15 dollars and
25 cents, 15 dollars and 35 cents.

---

28. Peter has a $1 bill, 2 dimes, and a nickel.

He has _____ dollar and _____ cents or $_____.

29. Alexa has a $20 bill, 2 quarters, and a dime.

She has _____ dollars and _____ cents or $_____.

Count the money.
Fill in the missing amounts.

Example

40¢ = $_0.40_.

30.

27¢ = $_____

31.

315¢ = $_____

32.

1,000¢ = $_____

Count the money.
Fill in the missing amounts.

> ### Example
>
>
>
> $0.45 = ___*45*___ ¢.

33.

$0.90 = _____¢

34.

$5.65 = _____¢

35.

$10.95 = _____¢

Worksheet 2 Comparing Amounts of Money

Compare.
Who has less?

Example

Shanice
$30.24

Dollars	Cents
30	24

Paige
$45.17

Dollars	Cents
45	17

$45.17 is more than $30.24.
$30.24 is less than $45.17.

So, _____*Shanice*_____ has less.

First, compare the dollars.
30 is less than 45.

Compare.
Who has less?

1.

Mike
$15.51

Dollars	Cents
15	51

Ava
$45.12

Dollars	Cents
45	12

$45.12 is more than $15.51.
$15.51 is less than $45.12.

So, _____ has less.

First, compare the dollars.

Name: _____   Date: _____

Compare.
Who has more?

┌─ **Example** ───┐

Liam
$12.25

Dollars	Cents
12	25

Kay
$12.10

Dollars	Cents
12	10

$12.25 is more than $12.10.
$12.10 is less than $12.25.

So, _____*Liam*_____ has more.

First, compare the dollars.
They are the same.
Then, compare the cents.
25 is greater than 10.

└──┘

Compare.
Who has more?

2.

Luis
$30.05

Dollars	Cents
30	05

Audrey
$30.15

Dollars	Cents
30	15

$30.15 is more than $30.05.
$30.05 is less than $30.15.

So, _____ has more.

First, compare the dollars.
They are the same.
Then, compare the cents.

Worksheet 3   Real-World Problems: Money

Solve.

Use bar models to help you.

Example

Peter has $23.

He saves $12 more.

He then spends $20.

How much money does Peter have left?

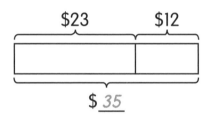

$23 + $12 = $_____35_____

Peter has $_____35_____ in all.

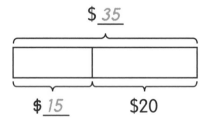

$35 – $20 = $_____15_____

Peter has $_____15_____ left.

Solve.
Use bar models to help you.

1.   Mr. Garcia has $458.
     He has $13 more than Mrs. Garcia.
     Mrs. Garcia spends $123.
     How much money does Mrs. Garcia have left?

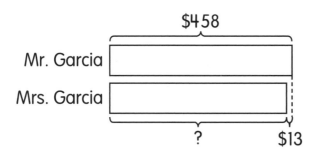

Mrs. Garcia has $_____ in all.

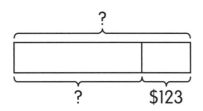

Mrs. Garcia has $_____ left.

Name: _____

Solve.
Use bar models to help you.

> **Example**
>
> Gillian bought an eraser, a pencil, and a ruler.
> The eraser cost 40¢, the pencil cost 55¢, and the ruler cost 85¢.
> How much did she pay in all?
>
>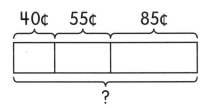
>
> 40¢ + 55¢ + 85¢ = _____180_____ ¢
>
>   = $_____1.80_____
>
> She paid $_____1.80_____ in all.

2. Esther bought a sandwich, a drink, and a granola bar.
    The sandwich cost $3, the drink cost $1,
    and the granola bar cost $2.
    How much did she pay in all?

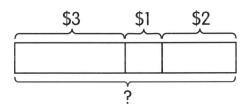

$3 + $1 + $2 = $_____

She paid $_____ in all.

Solve.
Draw bar models to help you.

3.   Kelly spent $16 on a book and $12 on a necklace.
      Then she had $10 left.
      How much money did Kelly have at first?

      Kelly had $_____ at first.

4.   Tristan bought a pair of pants for $25 and a T-shirt for $10.
      He had $70 at first.
      How much money did Tristan have left?

      Tristan had $_____ left.

Solve.

5.   Judy collects 5 nickels and 4 dimes.
           How much money has she collected?

           She has collected _____ ¢.

6.   Mrs. King has $7.45. She has 80¢ more than Mrs. Powell.
           How much money does Mrs. Powell have?

           Mrs. Powell has $_____.

7. Janet had 2 nickels, 5 pennies, and 3 dollar bills.
She spent $1.35.
How much money did Janet have left?

Janet had $_____ left.

8. After buying a loaf of bread for 2 dollar bills, 2 dimes, and
3 nickels, Jill has $2.10 left.
How much money did Jill have at first?

Jill had $_____ at first.

Fractions

Worksheet 1   Understanding Fractions

Look at the figures.
Then fill in the blanks.

Example

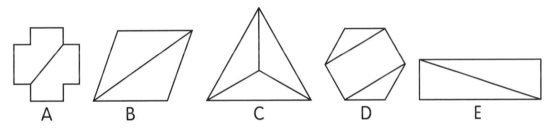

Figures _A, B, C, and E_ have equal parts.

Figure ___D___ has unequal parts.

1.

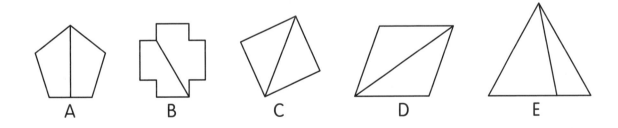

Figures _____ have equal parts.

Figure _____ has unequal parts.

Put an X in the box if the shape is divided into equal parts.

┌─ Example ──────────────────────────────────┐
│   │
│      ┌─────────┐ │
│   │   X   │ │
│   └─────────┘ │
└───┘

2.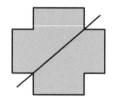

3.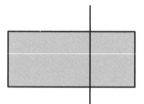

4.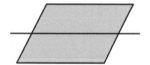

Divide the drawings into equal parts in 4 different ways.

┌─ Example ──────────────────────────────────┐
│   │
│   [ ] | [ ]   [ ]—[ ]   [◣�"]   [◢"]   │
│   │
└───┘

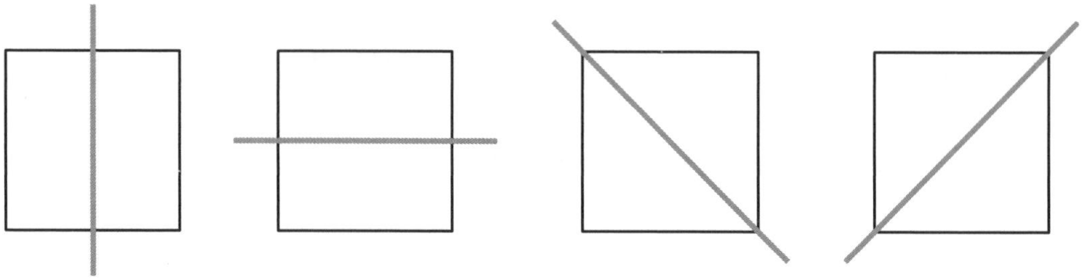

5.

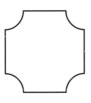

6.

Mark with an X the fractional parts that do not belong in each row.

Example

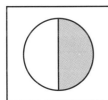   one-half

7.

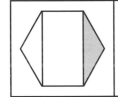 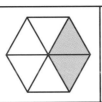 one-third

8.

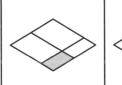 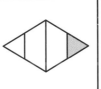 one-quarter

9.

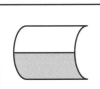   one-half

Write a fraction for each shaded part.

Example

$\dfrac{1}{3}$ _____

A **fraction** is a number that names equal parts of a whole. A whole describes an entire figure and is equal to one.

10.

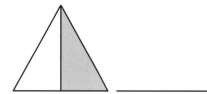 _____

11.

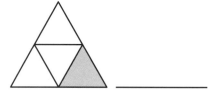 _____

Write the fraction for the shaded part or parts.

Example

$\dfrac{1}{4}$

_____ is shaded.

12.

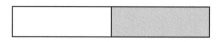

_____ is shaded.

13.

_____ is shaded.

14.

_____ is shaded.

Worksheet 2   Comparing Fractions

Write the fraction for the shaded part or parts.
Then compare the fractions.

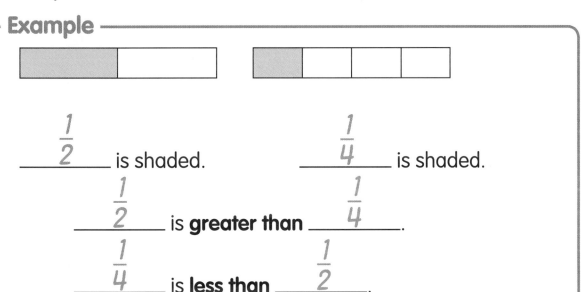

Example

$\dfrac{1}{2}$

_____ is shaded.

$\dfrac{1}{4}$

_____ is shaded.

$\dfrac{1}{2}$

_____ is **greater than** _____ $\dfrac{1}{4}$.

$\dfrac{1}{4}$

_____ is **less than** _____ $\dfrac{1}{2}$.

1.

_____ is shaded.   _____ is shaded.

_____ is greater than _____.

_____ is less than _____.

2.

_____ is shaded.   _____ is shaded.

_____ is greater than _____.

_____ is less than _____.

Color a copy of the model to show each fraction.
Then compare and fill in the blanks with > or <.

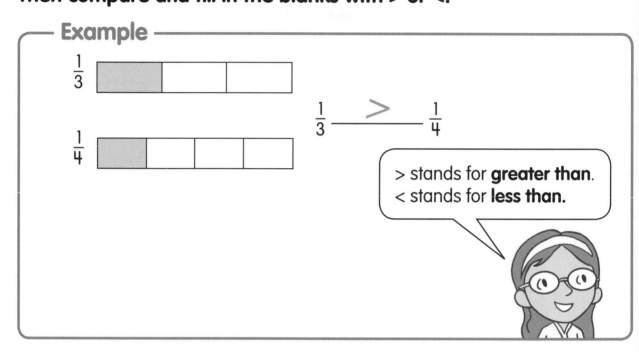

── Example ──

$\frac{1}{3}$

$\frac{1}{4}$

$\frac{1}{3}$ ──── > ──── $\frac{1}{4}$

> stands for **greater than**.
< stands for **less than**.

3. $\frac{1}{4}$

$\frac{1}{2}$

$\frac{1}{4}$ ──────── $\frac{1}{2}$

4. $\frac{1}{2}$

$\frac{1}{3}$

$\frac{1}{2}$ ──────── $\frac{1}{3}$

Worksheet 3   Adding and Subtracting
Like Fractions

Shade to show the fractions.

Example

$\frac{1}{2}$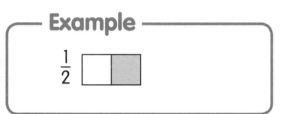

1. $\frac{2}{3}$

2. $\frac{1}{3}$

3. $\frac{3}{4}$

Write a fraction for the shaded parts.

Example

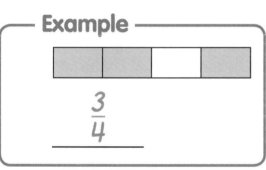

$\frac{3}{4}$
_____

4.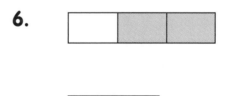

_____

5. _____

6. _____

Circle the like fractions.

┌─ **Example** ──┐

  $\frac{2}{2}$

$\frac{1}{4}$ and $\frac{3}{4}$ are **like fractions**. The bottom number is the same.

└──┘

7. $\frac{2}{3}$ $\frac{1}{2}$ $\frac{2}{2}$ **8.** $\frac{2}{2}$ $\frac{1}{3}$ $\frac{3}{3}$

9. $\frac{4}{4}$ $\frac{1}{2}$ $\frac{2}{4}$ **10.** $\frac{2}{3}$ $\frac{3}{3}$ $\frac{1}{4}$

Shade the parts to show the sum.

┌─ **Example** ──┐

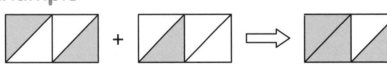

└──┘

11.

Add.
Use models to help you.

Example

$$\frac{1}{2} + \frac{1}{2} = \underline{\frac{2}{2} \text{ or } 1}$$

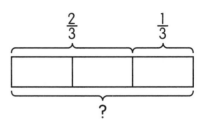

12. $\frac{2}{3} + \frac{1}{3} =$ _____

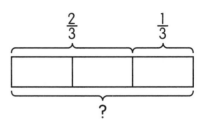

13. $\frac{1}{4} + \frac{1}{4} =$ _____

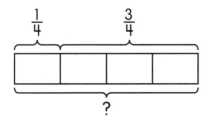

14. $\frac{2}{4} + \frac{1}{4} =$ _____

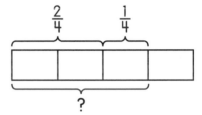

Add.
Use models to help you.

15. $\frac{1}{4} +$ _____ $= 1$

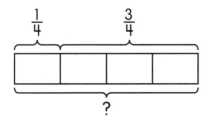

16. $\frac{1}{3} +$ _____ $= 1$

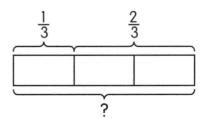

Shade the parts to show the difference.

Example

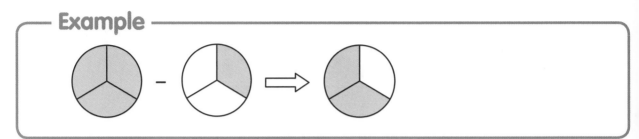

17.

Subtract.

Use models to help you.

Example

$$1 - \frac{2}{3} = \quad \frac{1}{3}$$

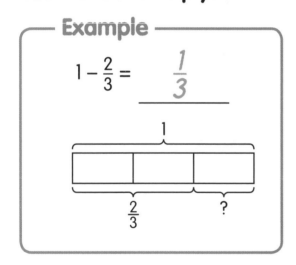

18. $\frac{2}{3} - \frac{1}{3} =$ _____

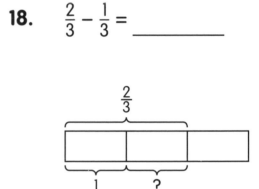

19. $\frac{3}{4} -$ _____ $= \frac{1}{4}$

20. $1 -$ _____ $= \frac{1}{2}$

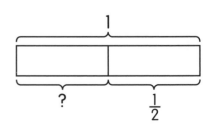

CHAPTER 13 Customary Measurement of Length

Worksheet 1 Measuring in Feet

Look at the drawing.
Then fill in each blank with *more* or *less*.

1.

The length of the paper clip is _____ than 1 centimeter.

2.

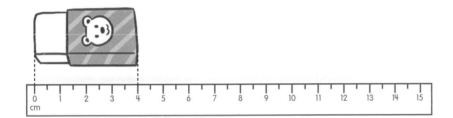

The length of the eraser is _____ than 3 centimeters.

3.

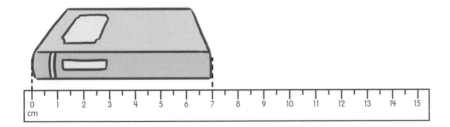

The length of the book is _____ than 10 centimeters.

> These rulers are smaller than in real life.

Name: _____ Date: _____

Look at each drawing.
Then fill in each blank with *more* or *less*.

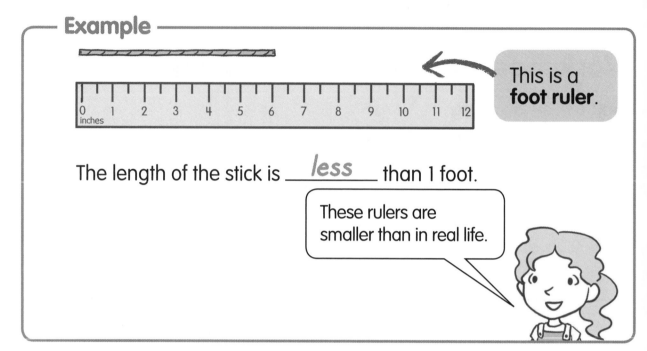

Example

The length of the stick is _____*less*_____ than 1 foot.

This is a **foot ruler**.

These rulers are smaller than in real life.

4.

The length of the frog is _____ than 1 foot.

5.

The length of the can of sardines is _____ than 1 foot.

Look at each drawing.
Then fill in each blank with *more* or *less*.

Example

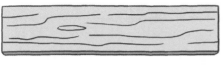 foot rulers

The length of the board is ___*more*___ than 2 feet.

6.

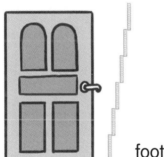

foot rulers

The length of the door is _____ than 6 feet.

7.

foot rulers

The height of the boy is _____ than 2 feet.

Name: _____ Date: _____

Look at the pictures.
Estimate and fill in the blanks.

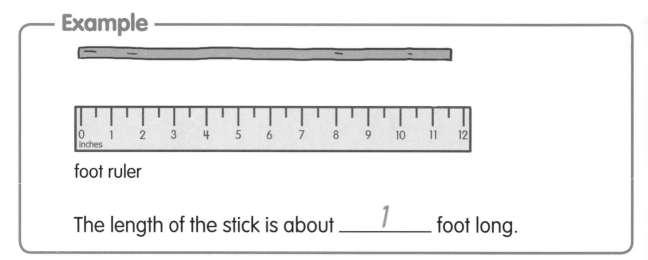

foot ruler

The length of the stick is about _____*1*_____ foot long.

8.

foot rulers

The length of the box is about _____ feet long.

9.

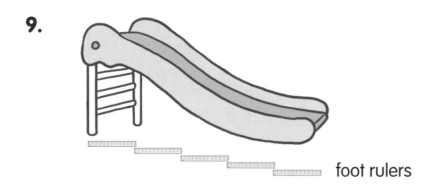

foot rulers

The length of the slide is about _____ feet long.

These rulers are smaller than in real life.

Worksheet 2   Comparing Lengths in Feet

Fill in the blanks with *taller* or *shorter*.

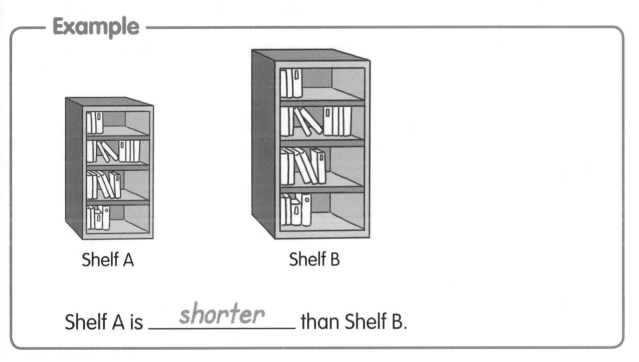

── Example ──

Shelf A   Shelf B

Shelf A is ____*shorter*____ than Shelf B.

1.

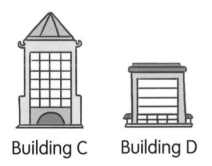

Building C   Building D

Building C is _____ than Building D.

Circle the longest measurement and check (✔) the shortest measurement.

┌─── **Example** ───┐

Rope A
24 ft

☐

Rope B
18 ft

☑ ✔

Rope C
34 ft

☐

The **foot** is a unit of length. **ft** stands for foot.

└──┘

2.

Tricycle A
4 ft

Tricycle B
5 ft

Tricycle C
3 ft

3.

Tree A
23 ft

Tree B
10 ft

Tree C
43 ft

Fill in the blanks.

Example

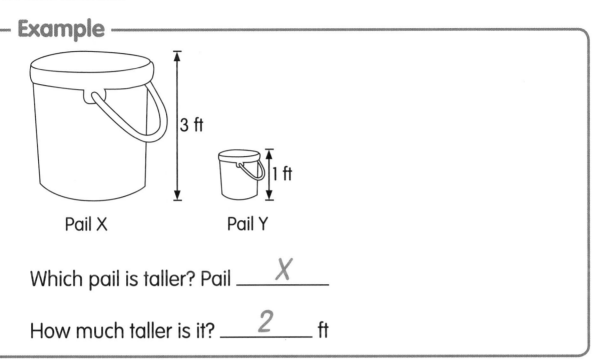

Pail X   Pail Y

Which pail is taller? Pail ____X____

How much taller is it? ____2____ ft

4.

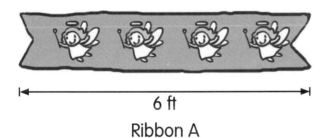

6 ft

Ribbon A

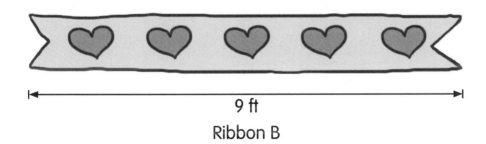

9 ft

Ribbon B

Which ribbon is shorter? Ribbon _____

How much shorter is it? _____ ft

5.

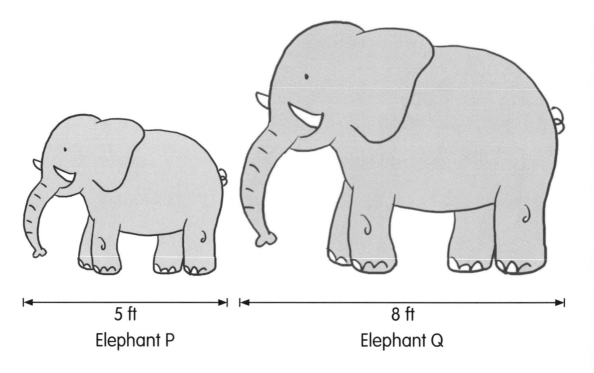

5 ft
Elephant P

8 ft
Elephant Q

Which elephant is longer? Elephant _____

How much longer is it? _____ ft

6.

4 ft

5 ft

Rosanne   Patricia

Which girl is taller? _____

How much taller is she? _____ ft

Worksheet 3   Measuring in Inches

Fill in the blanks.

Example

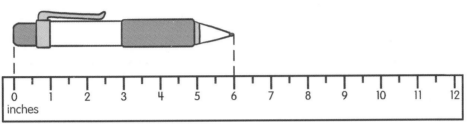

The pen is about _____ inches long.

These rulers are smaller than in real life.

The **inch** is a unit of length. **in.** stands for inch.

1.

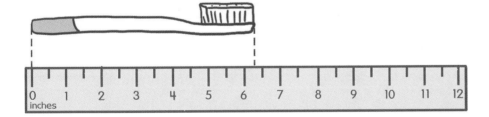

The toothbrush is about _____ inches long.

2.

The key is about _____ inches long.

Use a string and a ruler to measure each curve.
Then fill in the blanks.

Example

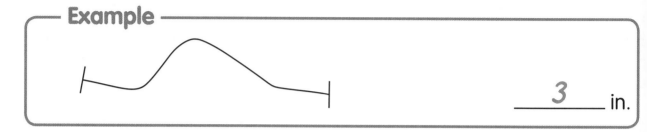

_____3_____ in.

3.

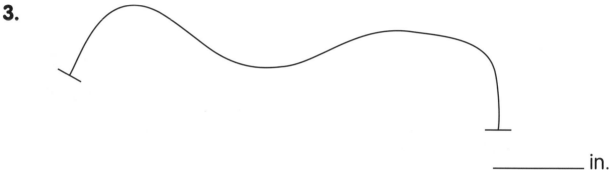

_____ in.

4.

_____ in.

5.

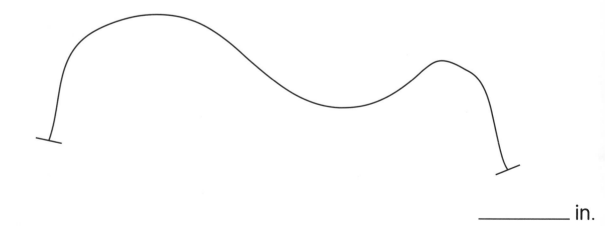

_____ in.

Use your inch ruler to draw.

┌─ Example ──┐
│   │
│   Part of a line A that is 3 inches long.   │
│   │
│   *Part of a line A* _____   │
│   │
└──┘

6. Part of a line B that is 2 inches long.

┌──┐
│   │
│   │
│   │
└──┘

7. Part of a line C that is 4 inches long.

┌──┐
│   │
│   │
│   │
└──┘

8. Part of a line D that is 3 inches long.

┌──┐
│   │
│   │
│   │
└──┘

Name: _____   Date: _____

Fill in the blanks.

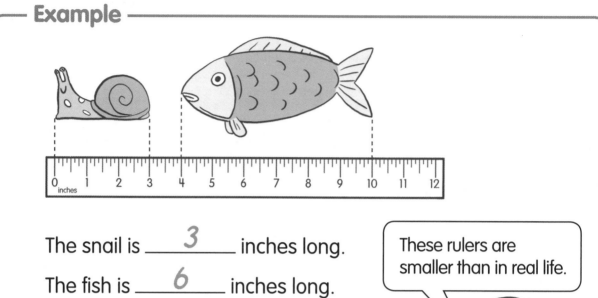

The snail is ___3___ inches long.

The fish is ___6___ inches long.

These rulers are smaller than in real life.

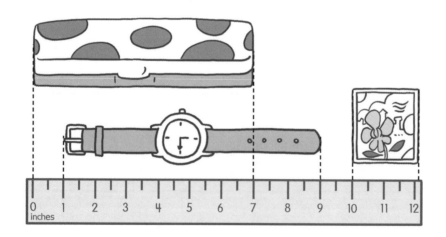

9.   The sticker is _____ inches long.

10.   The watch is _____ inches long.

11.   The glasses case is _____ inches long.

Worksheet 4   Comparing Lengths in Inches and Feet

Look at each drawing.
Then fill in the blanks.

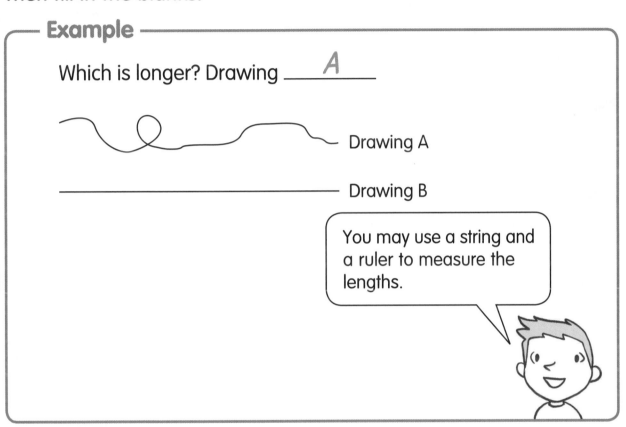

Example

Which is longer? Drawing ____*A*____

Drawing A

Drawing B

You may use a string and a ruler to measure the lengths.

1.   Which is the shortest?

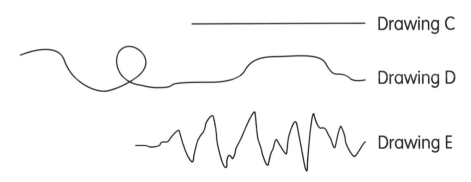

Drawing C

Drawing D

Drawing E

Drawing _____ is the shortest.

Fill in the blanks.

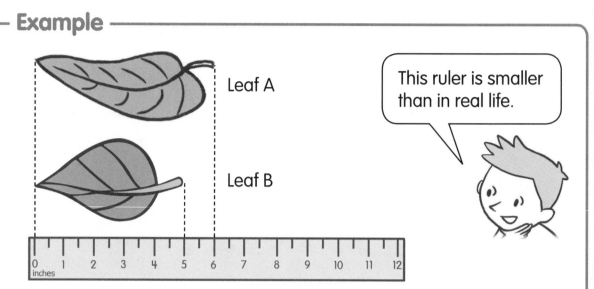

Example

Leaf A

Leaf B

This ruler is smaller than in real life.

Leaf A is ___6___ inches long.

Leaf B is ___5___ inches long.

___6___ – ___5___ = ___1___

Leaf ___B___ is ___1___ inch shorter than Leaf ___A___.

You can subtract to measure the difference in lengths.

2.

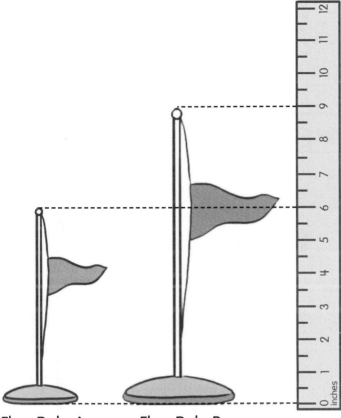

Flag Pole A   Flag Pole B

Flag Pole A is _____ inches long.

Flag Pole B is _____ inches long.

_____ – _____ = _____

Flag Pole _____ is _____ inches taller than

Flag Pole _____.

3.

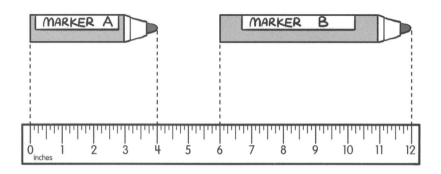

Marker A is _____ inches long.

Marker B is _____ inches long.

_____ − _____ = _____

Marker _____ is _____ inches longer than

Marker _____.

This ruler is smaller than in real life.

Lee measured some objects at home first in inches, then in feet. She recorded the measurements in a chart.

	in.	ft
height of my dog	22	2
length of my desk	38	3
length of the porch	84	7

4. Which objects do you think were easier to measure using feet?

5. Why are there fewer feet than inches when Lee measured the objects?

Worksheet 5   Real-World Problems: Customary Length

Solve.

Example

A school has two swimming pools.
The big pool is 40 feet long.
The small pool is 20 feet long.
What is the total length of both swimming pools?

$40 + 20 = 60$

The total length of both swimming pools is ___60___ feet.

---

1.   Gillian cycled 420 feet to the post office.
     She then cycled another 230 feet to the school.
     How far did Gillian cycle in all?

     Gillian cycled _____ feet in all.

2.   Roy measured 2 walking paths.
     Path A was 69 feet long.
     Path B was 164 feet long.
     What was the total length of the 2 walking paths?

     The total length of the 2 walking paths was _____ feet.

Name: _____ Date: _____

Solve.
Use bar models to help you.

┌─ **Example** ─────────────────────────────────────┐

A piece of ribbon, 136 inches long, is cut into 2 pieces.
One piece is 94 inches long.
How long is the other piece?

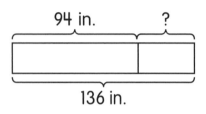

$\underline{\quad 136 \quad}$ – $\underline{\quad 94 \quad}$ = $\underline{\quad 42 \quad}$

The length of the other piece is ___42___ inches.

└──┘

3. A piece of string, 78 inches long, is cut into 2 pieces.
One piece measures 45 inches.
How long is the other piece of string?

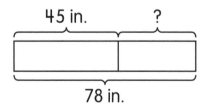

_____ – _____ = _____

The other piece of string is _____ inches long.

4. Dion is 70 inches tall.
His brother is 23 inches shorter than Dion.
How tall is Dion's brother?

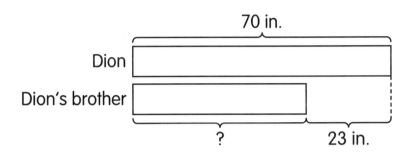

_____ − _____ = _____

Dion's brother is _____ inches tall.

5. Antonio is 62 inches tall.
His sister is 12 inches taller than Antonio.
How tall is Antonio's sister?

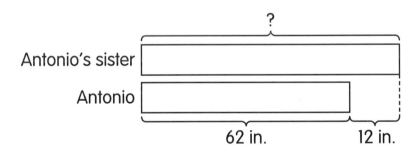

_____ + _____ = _____

Antonio's sister is _____ inches tall.

Solve.
Show your work.
Draw bar models to help you.

--- **Example** ---

Peter walked 56 feet.
He stopped to rest.
Then he walked another 42 feet.

a. How far did he walk in all?

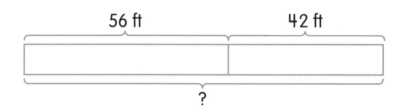

$$56 + 42 = 98$$

Peter walked ____98____ feet in all.

b. How much more did Peter walk before his rest than after his rest?

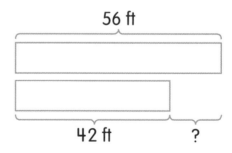

$$56 - 42 = 14$$

He walked ____14____ more feet before his rest.

6. Victoria is 65 inches tall.
Her sister is 15 inches shorter than Victoria.
How tall is Victoria's sister?

Victoria's sister is _____ inches tall.

7. The length of Rope A is 45 inches.
The length of Rope B is 34 inches longer than Rope A.

a. How long is Rope B?

Rope B is _____ inches long.

b. How long are both Rope A and Rope B in all?

Rope A and Rope B are _____ inches long in all.

8. The length of Train A is 145 feet.
The length of Train B is 89 feet longer than Train A.

a. How long is Train B?

Train B is _____ feet long.

b. What is the total length of both trains?

The total length of both trains is _____ feet.

Time

Worksheet 1   The Minute Hand

What is the time?

1.

It is _____ o'clock.

2.

It is half past _____.

Find the missing number.
Skip-count by 5s to help you.

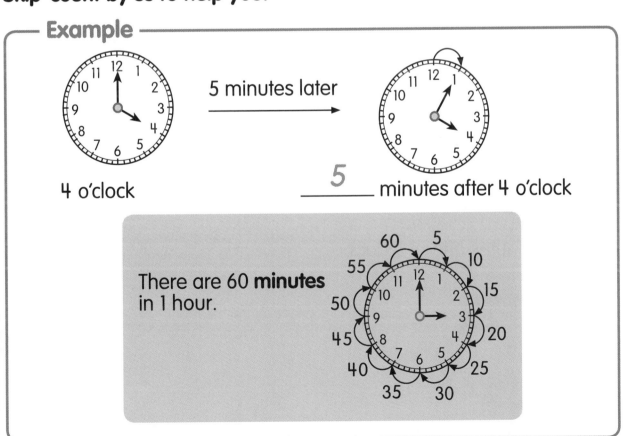

Example

4 o'clock → 5 minutes later → *5* minutes after 4 o'clock

There are 60 **minutes** in 1 hour.

3.

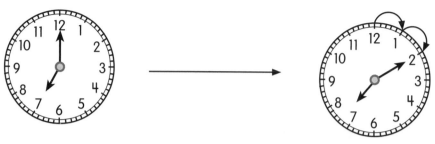

7 o'clock   _____ minutes after 7 o'clock

4.

6 o'clock   _____ minutes after 6 o'clock

Draw the minute hand to show the time.

5.   35 minutes after 2 o'clock

6.   50 minutes after 9 o'clock

Worksheet 2 Reading and Writing Time

Write the time.

Example

Sean is going to the zoo.
What time does he reach the zoo?

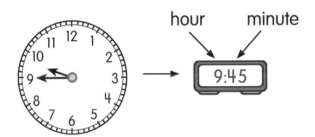

hour   minute

9:45

He reaches the zoo at ___9:45___.

He reaches the zoo at nine forty-five, or forty-five minutes after 9.

---

1.   Mrs. Eckles is going to the supermarket.
What time does she reach the supermarket?

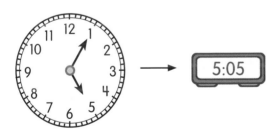

5:05

She reaches the supermarket at _____.

Circle the correct time.

2.

3:20   4:20   5:20

3.

1:35   2:35   2:55

Write the time in words.

┌─ **Example** ──────────────────────────────────────┐
│
│   `5:05`
│
│
│   _five-oh-five or 5 minutes after 5_
│
└──┘

4.   `4:35`

_____

5.   `7:15`

_____

Draw the minute hand to show the time.

6.   The time is 6:35.

7.   The time is 8:55.

8.   The time is 12:15.

9.   The time is 3:50.

Draw the hour hand to show the time.

10.   The time is 10:05.

11.   The time is 1:00.

12.   The time is 11:20.

13.   The time is 2:30.

Draw the hands to show the time.

14.   The time is 3:30.

15.   The time is 6:15.

16.   The time is 4:45.

17.   The time is 8:20.

Draw the hands to show the time.
Then write the time in words.

18.   The time is 12:35.

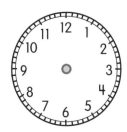

_____

19.   The time is 7:55.

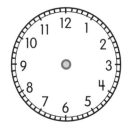

_____

Worksheet 3   Using A.M. and P.M.

Write A.M. or P.M.

Example

Tammy reaches the library at ten fifteen in the morning

or 10:15 ___A.M.___

> Use **A.M.** to talk about time after midnight to before noon.

She leaves the library at one thirty in the afternoon

or 1:30 ___P.M.___

> Use **P.M.** to talk about time after noon to before midnight.

---

1. Mr. Brass reaches home at 5 in the evening.

   The time is 5:00 _____.

2. Jamie is eating breakfast in the morning.

   The time is 6:45 _____.

3. Suzanne eats a snack in the afternoon.

   The time is 1:30 _____.

Read and write the time shown on each clock.
Use A.M. or P.M. to show the time of the day.

4. Samuel swims after school at _____.

5. Elric goes to sleep at _____ at night.

6. Mrs. Henderson goes to the bank at _____.

Order the times in Exercises 4 to 6.
Arrange them in order from the beginning of the day.

7.

_____, _____, _____
earliest

Worksheet 4   Elapsed Time

Complete.

Example

Kathy's art class starts at 11:00 A.M. and ends at 12:00 P.M.

Start	End	Lesson Time
11:00 A.M.	12:00 P.M.	1 hour

Kathy's lesson is __*1 hour*__ long.

---

1.   Bob starts swimming at 5:00 P.M. and ends at 6:00 P.M.

Start	End	Time Taken
5:00 P.M.	6:00 P.M.	1 hour

Bob swims for _____.

2.   Jeanie starts eating lunch at 12:00 P.M.
She finishes eating after an hour.

She finishes eating at _____.

Name: _____   **Date:** _____

Complete.

┌─ **Example** ──┐

Leslie goes to the park at 8:00 A.M. and leaves at 8:30 A.M.

Start	End	Time Taken
8:00 A.M.	8:30 P.M.	30 minutes

Leslie spends _30 minutes_ at the park.

└──┘

3. Minnie eats a snack at 1:00 P.M. and finishes at 1:30 P.M.

Start	End	Time Taken
1:00 P.M.	1:30 P.M.	30 minutes

Minnie eats a snack for _____.

4. Jules took a nap at 3:00 P.M.
She woke up after 30 minutes.

She woke up at _____.

CHAPTER 15 Multiplication Tables of 3 and 4

Worksheet 1   Multiplying 3: Skip-Counting

Use skip-counting to find the missing numbers.

1. $3 \times 2 =$ _____

2. $3 \times 5 =$ _____

3. $3 \times 10 =$ _____

Use skip-counting to find the missing numbers.

Example

There are 3 pencils in each bundle.
How many pencils are there in 5 bundles?

1, 2, <u>3</u>   4, 5, <u>6</u>   7, 8, <u>9</u>   10, 11, <u>12</u>   13, 14, <u>15</u>

3, 6, 9, 12, 15

$5 \times 3 =$ ___*15*___

There are ___*15*___ pencils.

Use skip-counting to find the missing numbers.

4. Nicky pastes 3 stickers on each page of his album.
His album has 10 pages.
How many stickers does Nicky paste in all?

3, 6, 9, 12, 15, 18, 21, 24, 27, 30

$10 \times 3 =$ _____

There are _____ stickers in all.

5. Valencia puts 3 tulips in each vase.
She has 3 vases.
How many tulips does Valencia have?

$$3 + 3 = 6$$
$$6 + 3 = ?$$

3, 6, _____

_____ $\times 3 =$ _____

Valencia has _____ tulips in all.

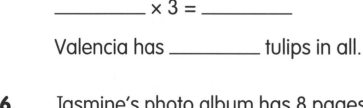

6. Jasmine's photo album has 8 pages.
There are 3 photos on each page.
How many photos are there in all?

_____ $\times 3 =$ _____

There are _____ photos in all.

Worksheet 2   Multiplying 3: Using Dot Paper

Use dot paper to solve.

1.   A farm has 6 hens.
     Each hen has 2 legs.
     How many legs do the hens have in all?

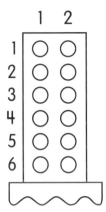

     _____ × _____ = _____

     The hens have _____ legs in all.

Use dot paper to find the missing numbers.

Example

There are 5 orchids.
Each orchid has 3 petals.
How many petals are there in all?

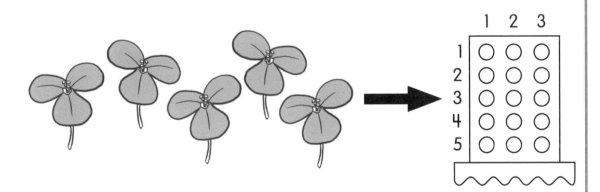

$5 \times 3 =$ ___*15*___

There are ___*15*___ petals in all.

2. Jon ties 3 balloons to each bench in his garden.
There are 3 benches in his garden.
How many balloons does Jon tie in all?

$3 \times 3 =$ _____

Jon ties _____ balloons in all.

3. Susan has 9 bowls.
She puts 3 plums in each bowl.
How many plums does Susan have in all?

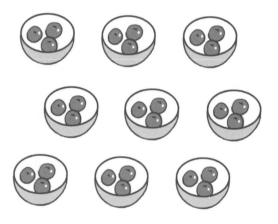

_____ $\times 3 =$ _____

Susan has _____ plums in all.

Use facts you know to find the missing numbers.

4.

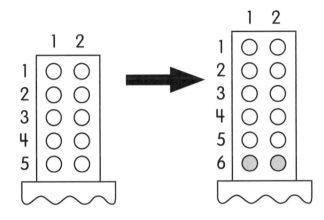

$5 \times 2 = 10$

$6 \times 2 = 10 +$ _____

$=$ _____

5.

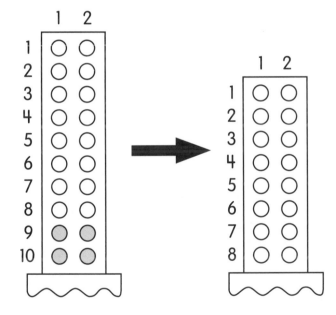

$10 \times 2 = 20$

$8 \times 2 = 20 -$ _____

$=$ _____

Use facts you know to find the missing numbers.

Example

$6 \times 3 = ?$

Start with 5 groups of 3.

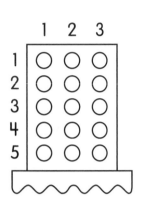

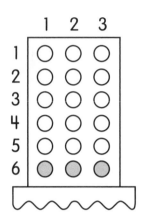

$5 \times 3 = 15$

$6 \times 3 = 15 + \underline{\quad 3 \quad}$

$= \underline{\quad 18 \quad}$

6. $7 \times 3 = ?$

Start with 5 groups of 3.

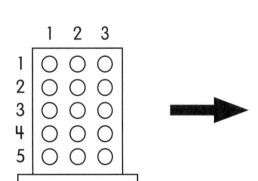

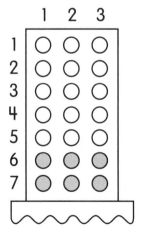

$5 \times 3 = 15$

$7 \times 3 = 15 + \underline{\qquad\qquad}$

$= \underline{\qquad\qquad}$

Use facts you know to find the missing numbers.

Example

8 × 3 = ?

Start with 10 groups of 3.

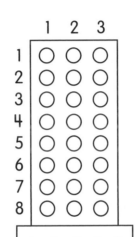

10 × 3 = 30

8 × 3 = 30 − _____6_____ = _____24_____

---

7.   9 × 3 = ?

Start with 10 groups of 3.

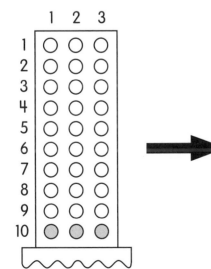

10 × 3 = 30

9 × 3 = 30 − _____ = _____

Use dot paper to find the missing numbers.

┌─── **Example** ───────────────────────────────────────┐

　　　　1　2　3

1 ○ ○ ○
2 ○ ○ ○
3 ○ ○ ○
4 ○ ○ ○

　　　　　1　2　3　4

1 ○ ○ ○ ○
2 ○ ○ ○ ○
3 ○ ○ ○ ○

4 × 3 = ___*12*___　　　　3 × 4 = ___*12*___

┌───┐
│ 4 × 3 = 3 × 4   │
│ These are **related multiplication facts**. │
└───┘

└───┘

8.

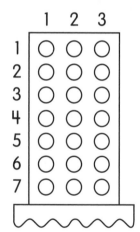

　　　　1　2　3

1 ○ ○ ○
2 ○ ○ ○
3 ○ ○ ○
4 ○ ○ ○
5 ○ ○ ○
6 ○ ○ ○
7 ○ ○ ○

　　　　　1　2　3　4　5　6　7

1 ○ ○ ○ ○ ○ ○ ○
2 ○ ○ ○ ○ ○ ○ ○
3 ○ ○ ○ ○ ○ ○ ○

7 × 3 = _____　　　　3 × 7 = _____

Worksheet 3   Multiplying 4: Skip-Counting

Use skip-counting to find the missing numbers.

1. $4 \times 2 =$ _____

2. $4 \times 5 =$ _____

3. $4 \times 10 =$ _____

Use skip-counting to find the missing numbers.

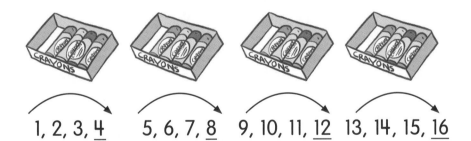

─ **Example** ─

Frida has 4 boxes of crayons.
Each box has 4 crayons.
How many crayons does Frida have in all?

1, 2, 3, <u>4</u>   5, 6, 7, <u>8</u>   9, 10, 11, <u>12</u>   13, 14, 15, <u>16</u>

4, 8, 12, 16

$4 \times 4 =$ _____*16*_____

Frida has _____*16*_____ crayons in all.

4. Tara buys 5 party hats.
Each party hat costs $4.
How much does Tara pay for the 5 party hats?

$4, $8, $12, $16, $20

5 × $4 = $_____

Tara pays $_____ for the 5 party hats.

5. Mrs. McGowan jogs 4 miles every day.
How many miles does she jog in a week?

4, 8, 12, 16, 20, 24, _____

_____ × 4 = _____

She jogs _____ miles in a week.

6. There are 8 rabbits in a field.
Each rabbit has 4 legs.
How many legs do the rabbits have in all?

_____ × 4 = _____

The rabbits have _____ legs in all.

Worksheet 4 Multiplying 4: Using Dot Paper

Use dot paper to solve.

1. Mina puts 2 cubes of ice into each cup.
    There are 5 cups.
    How many cubes of ice does Mina use?

    _____ × _____ = _____

    Mina uses _____ cubes of ice.

Use dot paper to find the missing numbers.

Example

There are 3 robin nests in a tree.
Each nest has 4 robin eggs.
How many robin eggs are there in all?

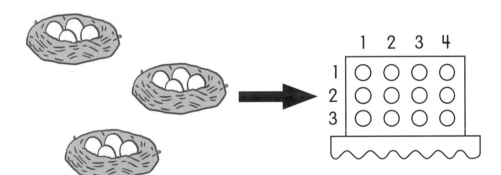

3 × 4 = ___*12*___

There are ___*12*___ robin eggs in all.

2.   Kelsey buys 7 tickets to a county fair.
Each ticket costs $4.
How much does Kelsey pay in all?

$7 \times \$4 = \$$_____

Kelsey pays $_____ in all.

3.   Eileen baked 9 boxes of muffins.
There are 4 muffins in each box.
How many muffins did Eileen bake in all?

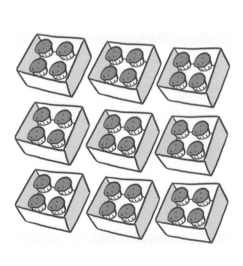

_____ $\times 4 =$ _____

Eileen baked _____ muffins in all.

Use facts you know to find the missing numbers.

4.

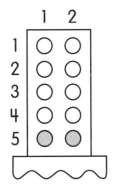

$5 \times 2 = 10$

$4 \times 2 = 10 -$ _____

$=$ _____

5.

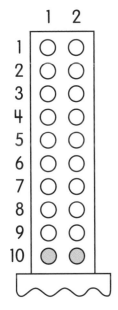

$10 \times 2 = 20$

$9 \times 2 = 20 -$ _____

$=$ _____

Use facts you know to find the missing numbers.

> **Example**
>
> $6 \times 4 = ?$
>
> Start with 5 groups of 4.
>
>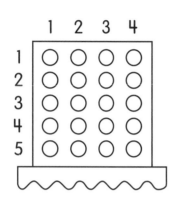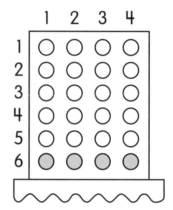
>
> $5 \times 4 = 20$ $6 \times 4 = 20 +$ ___4___
>
> $=$ ___24___

6. $7 \times 4 = ?$

Start with 5 groups of 4.

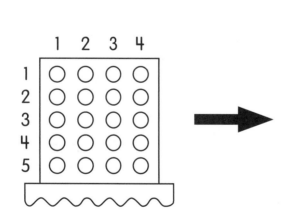   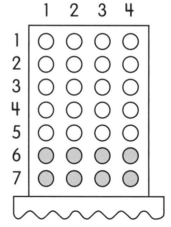

$5 \times 4 = 20$ $7 \times 4 = 20 +$ _____

$=$ _____

Use facts you know to find the missing numbers.

Example

$8 \times 4 = ?$

Start with 10 groups of 4.

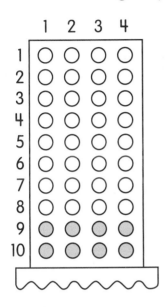

$10 \times 4 = 40$

$8 \times 4 = 40 - \underline{\quad 8 \quad} = \underline{\quad 32 \quad}$

7. $9 \times 4 = ?$

Start with 10 groups of 4.

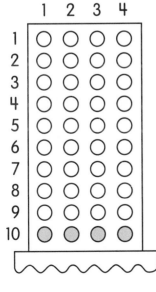

$10 \times 4 = 40$

$9 \times 4 = 40 - \underline{\qquad\qquad} = \underline{\qquad\qquad}$

Use dot paper to find the missing numbers.

Example

1 2 3 4

1 2
2

$2 \times 4 = $ _____ 8

1 2
1
2
3
4

$4 \times 2 = $ _____ 8

$2 \times 4 = 4 \times 2$
These are **related multiplication facts**.

8.

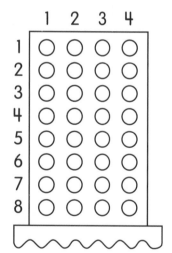

$8 \times 4 = $ _____

$4 \times 8 = $ _____

Worksheet 5   Divide Using Related Multiplication Facts

Use related multiplication facts to solve.

1.   Divide 10 forks into 2 equal groups.
How many forks are in each group?

_____ forks are in each group.

Find the missing numbers.
Use related multiplication facts to help you divide.

Example

Divide 15 buttons into equal groups.
There are 3 groups.
How many buttons are in each group?

$3 \times 5 = 15$

So, $15 \div 3 = \underline{\quad 5 \quad}$

$15 \div 3 = \underline{\quad 5 \quad}$

There are __5__ buttons in each group.

---

2.   Divide 28 eggs into 4 groups.
How many eggs are there in each group?

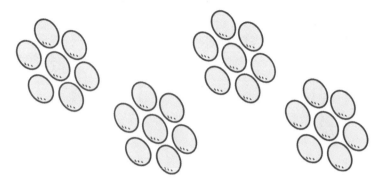

$4 \times 7 = 28$

So, $28 \div 4 =$ _____

Each group has _____ eggs.

3.   Divide 30 paper clips into 3 groups.
How many paper clips are there in each group?

$3 \times 10 = 30$

So, $30 \div 3 =$ _____

Each group has _____ paper clips.

Find the missing numbers.
Use related multiplication facts to help you divide.

Example

Joshua puts 9 cherries equally into bowls.
There are 3 cherries in each bowl.
How many bowls are there?

$3 \times 3 = 9$

So, $9 \div 3 =$ ___*3*___

$9 \div 3 =$ ___*3*___

There are ___*3*___ bowls.

---

4.   There are 24 snails on leaves.
There are 6 snails on each leaf.
How many leaves are there?

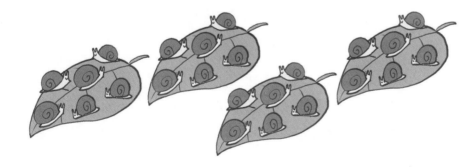

$4 \times 6 = 24$

So, $24 \div 6 =$ _____

There are _____ leaves.

Use related multiplication facts to solve.

5.   Bernard gives a total of $20 equally to 5 children.
How much does each child get?

Each child gets $_____.

6.   Sally puts 8 teddy bears onto shelves.
Each shelf has 4 teddy bears.
How many shelves are there?

There are _____ shelves.

7.   Donna picks a total of 30 peaches from 10 trees.
She picks the same number of peaches from each tree.
How many peaches does Donna pick from each tree?

Donna picks _____ peaches from each tree.

Name: _____ Date: _____

CHAPTER 16

Using Bar Models: Multiplication and Division

Worksheet 1   Real-World Problems: Multiplication

1. $6 \times 2 =$ _____

2. $5 \times 3 =$ _____

3. $9 \times 4 =$ _____

4. $8 \times 5 =$ _____

5. $7 \times 10 =$ _____

Solve. Use bar models to help you.

Example

3 □ are in each bag.
There are 3 bags.
How many □ are there in all?

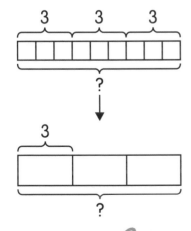

3   3   3

?

3

?

3 groups of 3 □.
3 + 3 + 3 or 3 × 3.
So, multiply to
find the answer.

$3 \times 3 =$ ___9___

There are ___9___ □ in all.

6. There are 6 dog biscuits in each bag.
There are 2 bags in all.
How many dog biscuits are there in all?

Use ☐ to show the number of dog biscuits.

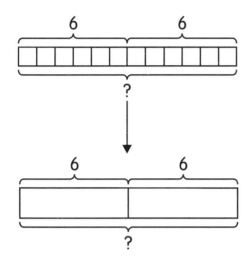

$2 \times 6 =$ _____

There are _____ dog biscuits in all.

7. Teresa makes 4 bracelets.
Each bracelet has 4 beads.
How many beads does Teresa use in all?

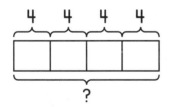

$4 \times 4 =$ _____

Teresa uses _____ beads in all.

Worksheet 2   Real-World Problems: Division

1.   14 ÷ 2 = _____

2.   15 ÷ 3 = _____

3.   20 ÷ 4 = _____

4.   45 ÷ 5 = _____

5.   80 ÷ 10 = _____

Solve.

Use bar models to help you.

Example

Suzi has 18 marbles in a bag.

She shares the marbles equally among 3 of her friends.

How many marbles does each friend receive?

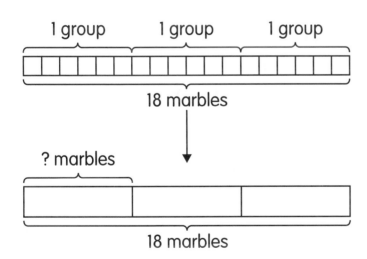

Use ☐ to show the number of marbles.

18 ÷ 3 = ___*6*___

Suzi's friends received ___*6*___ marbles each.

6. Penny has 15 pens.
She puts an equal number of pens into 3 pencil cases.
How many pens are there in each pencil case?

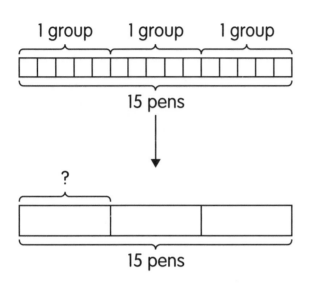

$15 \div 3 =$ _____

Each pencil case has _____ pens.

7. A farmer puts 32 eggs onto 4 trays.
Each tray has the same number of eggs.
How many eggs are there on each tray?

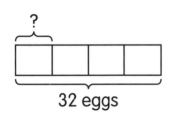

$32 \div 4 =$ _____

Each tray has _____ eggs.

Name: _____ **Date:** _____

Solve.
Use bar models to help you.

Example

Jason puts 10 cats into rooms.
He puts 5 cats into each room.
How many rooms are there?

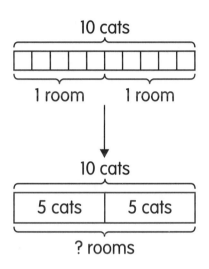

10 cats

1 room 1 room

10 cats

| 5 cats | 5 cats |

? rooms

Each room has 5 cats.
$5 \times ? = 10$
$5 \times 2 = 10$
So, there are 2 rooms.

$10 \div 5 =$ _____2_____

There are _____2_____ rooms.

8. Sasha puts 16 hair clips into some boxes.
Each box has 2 hair clips.
How many boxes are there?

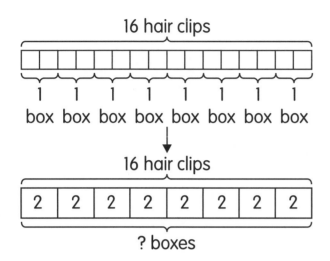

Use ☐ to show the number of hair clips.

16 ÷ 2 = _____

There are _____ boxes.

9. Julie puts 8 tea bags into some cups.
Each cup has 2 tea bags.
How many cups does Julie have?

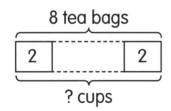

8 ÷ 2 = _____

Julie has _____ cups.

Worksheet 3   Real-World Problems: Measurement and Money

Solve.

Use bar models to help you.

Example

3 sticks are each 5 feet long.

They are placed end to end to make a long stick.

How long is the long stick?

5 ft

? ft

$3 \times 5 =$ ___15___

The long stick is ___15___ feet long.

---

1.   A carpenter had a wooden block.
     She cut the block into 4 pieces.
     Each piece of wood was 4 inches long.
     How long was the wooden block?

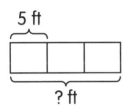

4 in.

? in.

$4 \times 4 =$ _____

The wooden block was _____ inches long.

Name: _____   **Date:** _____

Solve.
Use bar models to help you.

┌─── **Example** ───────────────────────────────────┐

A toy train is made up of 7 parts.
Each part is the same length.
The train is 70 centimeters long.
What is the length of each part?

? cm

[bar model divided into 7 equal parts, labeled 70 cm underneath]

$70 \div 7 =$ ___*10*___

The length of each part is ___*10*___ centimeters.

└───┘

2.   The total length of a piece of rope is 45 meters.
      The rope is cut into equal pieces that are 9 meters long.
      How many pieces of rope are there?

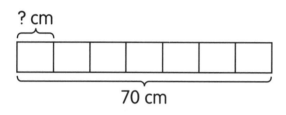

$45 \div 9 =$ _____

There are _____ pieces of rope.

Solve.
Use bar models to help you.

┌─ **Example** ───┐

Susanna has 4 coins.
The mass of each coin is 10 grams.
What is the mass of all the coins?

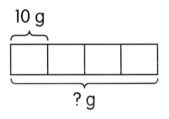

$4 \times 10 =$ _____40_____

The mass of all the coins is _____40_____ grams.

└───┘

3.   The mass of each melon is 3 kilograms.
What is the total mass of 4 melons?

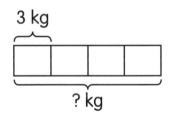

$4 \times 3 =$ _____

The total mass of 4 melons is _____ kilograms.

Solve.
Use bar models to help you.

Example

The total mass of 3 loaves of bread is 30 grams.
Each loaf of bread has the same mass.
What is the mass of each loaf of bread?

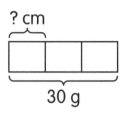

? cm

30 g

$30 \div 3 =$ ____10____

The mass of each loaf is ___10___ grams.

---

4. The total mass of some bags of soil is 25 kilograms.
    The mass of each bag of soil is 5 kilograms.
    How many bags of soil are there?

25 kg

| 5 | | 5 |

? bags

$25 \div 5 =$ _____

There are _____ bags of soil.

Solve.
Use bar models to help you.

> **Example**
>
> A bottle can hold 2 liters of water.
> It takes 5 of these bottles to fill a container.
> How many liters of water can the container hold?
>
>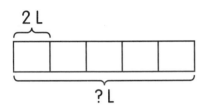
>
> 2 L
>
> ? L
>
> $5 \times 2 =$ ___10___
>
> The container can hold ___10___ liters of water.

5. Dan has 4 bottles.
   Each bottle has 3 liters of water.
   How many liters of water do the bottles have in all?

   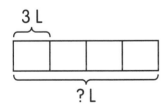

   3 L

   ? L

   $4 \times 3 =$ _____

   The bottles have _____ liters of water in all.

Solve.
Use bar models to help you.

┌─ **Example** ─────────────────────────────────────┐

Randy drinks 14 liters of water in a week.
He drinks the same amount of water each day.
How many liters of water does he drink every day?

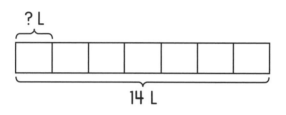

? L

14 L

$14 \div 7 =$ _____2_____

He drinks _____2_____ liters of water everyday.

└──┘

6.   Mr. Levan uses 24 liters of paint to paint some rooms.
He uses 4 liters of paint to paint each room.
How many rooms does Mr. Levan paint?

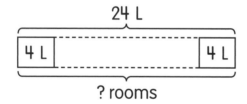

24 L

4 L   4 L

? rooms

$24 \div 4 =$ _____

Mr. Levan paints _____ rooms.

Solve.
Use bar models to help you.

┌─ **Example** ───┐

Gillian buys 4 erasers.
Each eraser costs 10¢.
How much does Gillian pay in all?

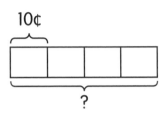

$4 \times 10¢ =$ _____40_____ ¢

She pays _____40_____ ¢ in all.

└───┘

7.   Kane saves $4 every day for a week.
How much does she save in 1 week?

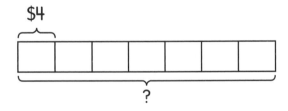

$7 \times \$4 = \$$_____

She saves $_____ in 1 week.

Solve.
Use bar models to help you.

Example

Mrs. Steven has $45.
She gives all of it equally to her 5 children.
How much money does each child get?

?
⎧‾‾‾‾‾‾‾‾⎫
| | | | | |
⎩_____⎭
$45

$45 ÷ 5 = $___9___

Each child gets $___9___.

---

8.   Mrs. Nelson has $27.
She divides the money equally among her children.
Each child gets $9.
How many children does Mrs. Nelson have?

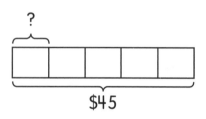

27 ÷ 9 = _____

Mrs. Nelson has _____ children.

Graphs and Line Plots

Worksheet 1   Reading Picture Graphs with Scales

Fill in the blanks.
Use the picture graph to help you.

Our Pets

Rabbit	Dog	Cat	Gerbil

Each ◯ stands for 1 animal.

1.   There are _____ types of pets.

2.   There are _____ dogs.

3.   There are _____ more rabbits than gerbils.

4.   There are _____ pets in all.

Each ♥ stands for 2 units.
Count and fill in the blanks.

Example

♥ ♥ ♥ ♥ stands for ____*8*____ units.

There are 4 ♥.
1 ♥ stands for 2 units.
4 × 2 = 8

5.   ♥ ♥ ♥ stands for _____ units.

6.   ♥ ♥ ♥ ♥ ♥ ♥ stands for _____ units.

Each ♦ stands for 5 units.
Count and fill in the blanks.

7.   ♦ ♦ stands for _____ units.

8.   ♦ ♦ ♦ ♦ ♦ stands for _____ units.

9.   ♦ ♦ ♦ ♦ ♦ ♦ ♦ stands for _____ units.

Multiply by 5 to
find the answer.

Name: _____   Date: _____

The picture graph shows the number of items sold at a bookshop
on a Monday.

Items Sold at a Bookshop

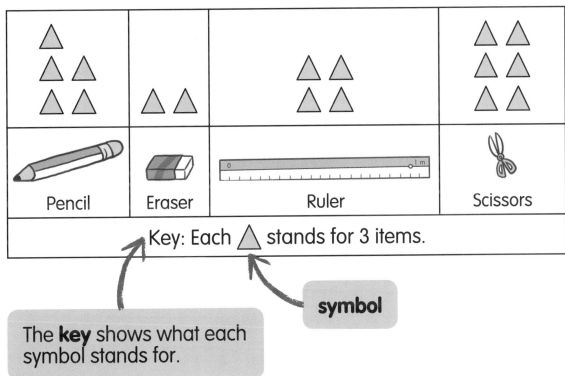

Key: Each △ stands for 3 items.

symbol

The **key** shows what each
symbol stands for.

Fill in the blanks.
Use the picture graph to help you.

--- **Example** ---

How many pencils were sold?

__15__

There are 5 △.
1 △ stands for 3 items.
5 × 3 = 15

Fill in the blanks.
Use the picture graph on page 129 to help you.

10.   How many pairs of scissors were sold? _____

11.   How many more pencils than erasers were sold? _____

12.   How many fewer rulers than scissors were sold? _____

13.   How many erasers and rulers were sold in all? _____

Count the △ for the erasers and rulers.
Then multiply to find the answer.

Name: _____ Date: _____

The picture graph shows the number of each kind of tableware in Mr. Martin's kitchen cabinet.

Mr. Martin's Tableware

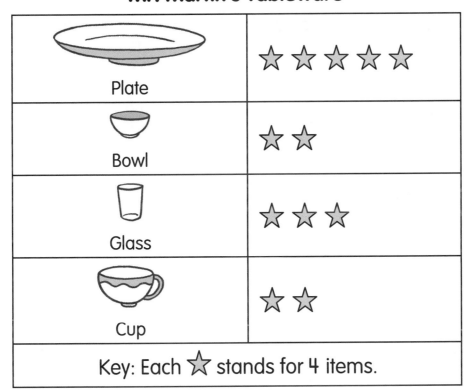

Key: Each ☆ stands for 4 items.

Use the graph to fill in the blanks.

14. There are _____ glasses.

15. The number of _____ is the same as the number of

_____.

16. The number of _____ is the most.

17. There are _____ fewer cups than plates.

18. Mr. Martin buys 8 more glasses.

He should draw _____ more ☆ on the graph.

The students in the second grade class have different after-school activities on Tuesday.
The picture graph shows the number of students in each activity.

After-School Activities of the Second Grade Class

jogging	☺ ☺
swimming	☺ ☺ ☺ ☺
skating	☺ ☺
dancing	☺

Key: Each ☺ stands for 3 students.

Use the graph to fill in the blanks.

19. _____ students swim after school.

20. The number of students who _____ is the same as the

    number of students who _____.

21. The number of students who _____ is the least.

22. There are _____ fewer students who jog than swim.

23. 8 boys swim after school.

    How many girls swim after school? _____

24. 3 students decide to skate rather than swim.

    How many students skate now? _____

Worksheet 2   Making Picture Graphs

1. **Count the animals in the picture.**
   Then complete the tally chart.

Animal	Tally	Number of Animals
Duck	⊮⊮	5
Turtle		
Dragonfly		
Flamingo		

Each ◯ stands for 5 units.
Draw ◯ to show the number of units.

┌─ Example ──┐
│   │
│ ┌──────────────┐   │
│ │ ◯ ◯ ◯ │ stand for 15 units.   ┌──────────────────┐ │
│ └──────────────┘   │ 1 ◯ stands for 5 units. │
│   │ $15 \div 5 = 3$ │
│    │ Draw 3 ◯.   │
│   └──────────────────┘ │
│   │
└──┘

2. ┌──────────────────┐ stand for 10 units.
     │   │
     └──────────────────┘

3. ┌──────────────────┐ stand for 40 units.
     │   │
     └──────────────────┘

Each △ stands for 3 units.
Draw △ to show the number of units.

4. ┌──────────────────┐ stand for 9 units.
     │   │
     └──────────────────┘

5. ┌──────────────────┐ stand for 12 units.
     │   │
     └──────────────────┘

6. ┌──────────────────┐ stand for 21 units.
     │   │
     └──────────────────┘

7. Mrs. Stanton bought some fruit.
Count how many pieces of fruit she bought.
Then complete the tally chart.

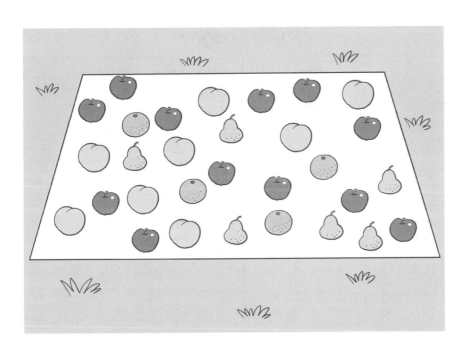

Fruit	Tally	Pieces of Fruits
Orange	////	4
Apple		
Peach		
Pear		

8. Use your answers on page 135.
Show the number of pieces of fruit by coloring the  in the picture graph.

Fruits Bought

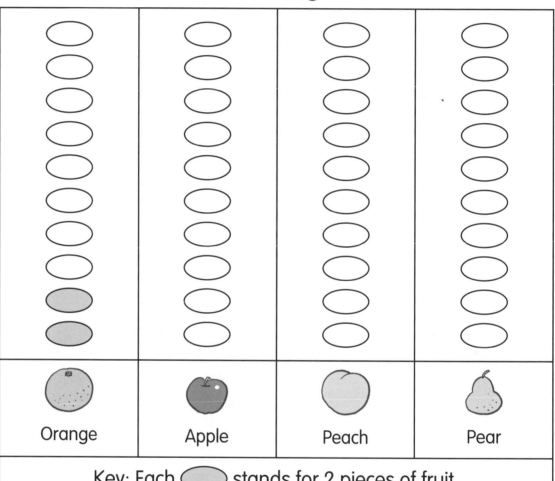

Key: Each ⬭ stands for 2 pieces of fruit.

1 ⬭ stands for 2 pieces.
There are 4 oranges.
$4 \div 2 = 2$
Color 2 ⬭.

9. The pictures show the favorite sport of each child in the second grade class.
Count the number of children who like each sport.
Then complete the tally chart.

Sport	Tally	Number of Children
Baseball		
Basketball		
Soccer		
Tennis		

10. Use your answers on page 137 to complete the picture graph. Then give the picture graph a title.

Title: _____

 Baseball	
 Basketball	
 Soccer	
 Tennis	
Key: Each ⬭ stands for 3 children.	

Worksheet 3 Real-World Problems: Picture Graphs

Use the picture graphs to answer the questions.

The picture graph shows the number of stamps five children have.

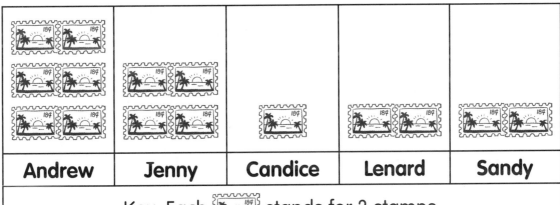

Stamp Collection of Five Children

Andrew	Jenny	Candice	Lenard	Sandy

Key: Each [stamp] stands for 3 stamps.

1. How many stamps does Andrew have? _____

2. Which two children have the same number of stamps?

    _____ and _____

3. How many more stamps does Jenny have than Lenard?

    _____

4. How many stamps do they have in all? _____

The picture graph shows the number of books Joel read in four months. Some information in the picture graph is missing.

Number of Books Read

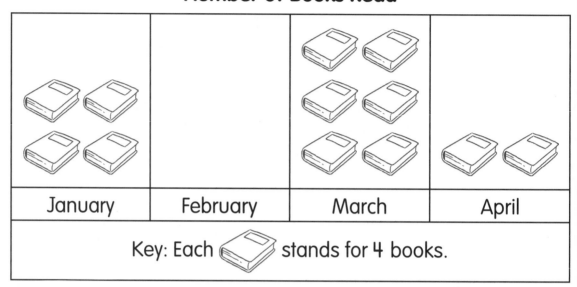

5.   Joel read 12 books in February.

How many 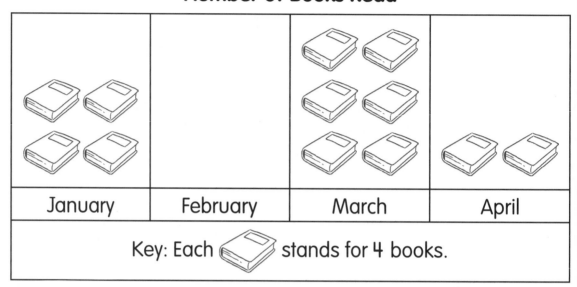 should be on the graph for February?

_____

6.   Joel read 20 books in April.

How many more 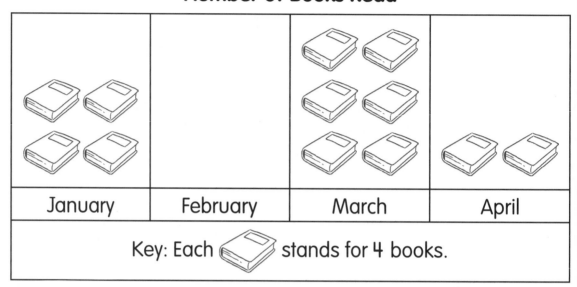 should be on the graph for April?

_____

7.   What is the total number of books that Joel read in

February and April? _____

Use the picture graph to fill in the blanks.

The picture graph shows the number of ideas from five classes during the School Innovation Week.

Ideas for School Innovation Week

Class A	🔆 🔆 🔆 🔆
Class B	🔆 🔆 🔆 🔆 🔆 🔆 🔆 🔆
Class C	🔆 🔆 🔆 🔆 🔆
Class D	🔆 🔆
Class E	🔆 🔆 🔆 🔆

Key: Each 🔆 stands for 2 ideas.

8. Class B had _____ more ideas than Class D.

9. Class _____ and Class _____ had more than 8 ideas.

10. Class _____ and Class _____ both had _____ ideas.

11. For Class C, 4 of the ideas are from the girls and _____ ideas are from the boys.

Doris asks some friends what color they like best. The tally chart shows the results.

12. Use the tally chart to complete the picture graph.

Color	Tally
Blue	卌 卌 卌
Green	卌 |
Red	卌 ||||
Orange	卌 |

Title: _____

▢ ▢ ▢	▢ ▢	▢	
Blue	**Green**	**Red**	**Orange**
Key: Each ▢ stands for 3 friends.			

13. Of the children who like green best, 4 are girls.

How many boys like green? _____

14. 12 boys chose blue or orange.

How many girls chose blue or orange? _____

Worksheet 4   Bar Graphs and Line Plots

The chart shows the months of students' birthdays from
January to May.

Student	Birthday Month	Student	Birthday Month
A	May	G	February
B	January	H	March
C	April	I	March
D	February	J	April
E	January	K	March
F	April	L	April

1.   Complete the table using the data.

Months	Number of Students
January	
February	
March	
April	
May	

2.   Use the data in the table to complete the line plot.

←————————————————————————→
    Jan   Feb   Mar   April   May

Students' Birthday Months

Use the line plot on page 143 to answer the questions.

3. How many students took the survey in all? _____

4. Which month has students with the greatest number of

birthdays? _____

5. Which month has students with the least number of birthdays?

_____

6. Two more students join the survey.
They are born in the same month.
This changes the month with the most birthdays.
In which month were these two students born?

_____

7. Draw the information from the line plot as a bar graph.

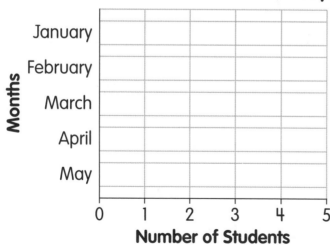

Months of Students' Birthdays

CHAPTER 18 Lines and Surfaces

Worksheet 1   Parts of Lines and Curves

Look at these drawings.
Then answer each question.

Example

 A   B    C   D

Which are parts of lines? __*A and D*__

Which are curves? __*B and C*__

This is a **part of a line**.   This is a **curve**.

1.   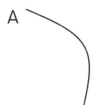 A   B   C    D

    a.   Which are parts of lines? _____

    b.   Which are curves? _____

Name: _____ **Date:** _____

Look at the drawings.
Count the number of parts of lines and curves.

Example

There are ____4____ parts of lines and ____2____ curves.

2.

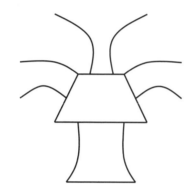

There are _____ parts of lines and _____ curves.

3.

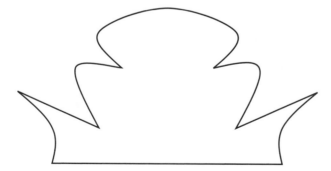

There are _____ parts of lines and _____ curves.

Worksheet 2   Flat and Curved Surfaces

Look at these drawings.
Then circle the drawings that have flat surfaces.

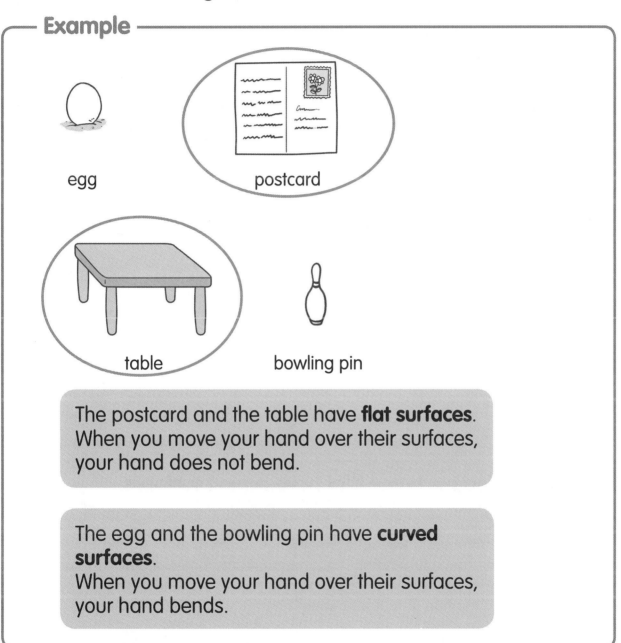

Example

egg

postcard

table

bowling pin

The postcard and the table have **flat surfaces**.
When you move your hand over their surfaces,
your hand does not bend.

The egg and the bowling pin have **curved surfaces**.
When you move your hand over their surfaces,
your hand bends.

Look at these drawings.
Then circle the drawings that have curved surfaces.

1.

book

baseball

eraser

watermelon

Name two objects at home that have flat surfaces.

2. _____

Name two objects at home that have curved surfaces.

3. _____

Look at the drawings.
Then circle the objects that can slide.

Example

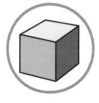

cube

pyramid

sphere

cone

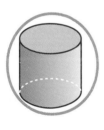

cylinder

rectangular prism

You can **slide** objects that have a flat surface.

Look at the drawings.
Then circle the objects that can stack.

4.

cylinder

cone

pyramid

cube

> You can **stack** objects that have more than one flat surface.

Look at the drawings.
Then circle the objects that can roll.

5.

cone

rectangular prism

sphere

cube

> You can **roll** objects that have curved surfaces.

CHAPTER 19 Shapes and Patterns

Worksheet 1 Plane Shapes

Look at the pictures.
Count and check (✔) the plane shapes that make up each picture.

Example

Plane Shape	Check (✔)	Number
Triangle	✔	3
Square	✔	2
Rectangle	✔	1
Circle	✔	1

1.

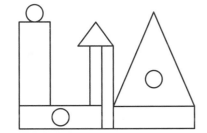

Plane Shape	Check (✔)	Number
Triangle		
Square		
Rectangle		
Circle		

2.

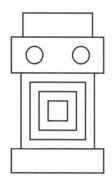

Plane Shape	Check (✔)	Number
Triangle		
Square		
Rectangle		
Circle		

Look at the pictures.

Then write down the number of plane shapes used in each picture.

Example

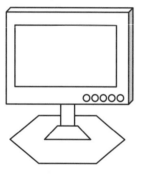

Plane Shape	Number
Triangle	0
Square	0
Rectangle	5
Circle	5
Hexagon	1
Trapezoid	1

A **trapezoid** () has __4__ sides.
A **hexagon** ( ) has __6__ sides.

3.

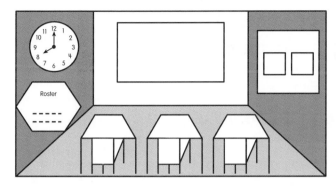

Plane Shape	Number
Triangle	
Square	
Rectangle	
Circle	
Hexagon	
Trapezoid	

4.

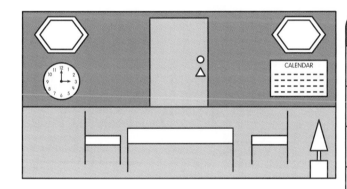

Plane Shape	Number
Triangle	
Square	
Rectangle	
Circle	
Hexagon	
Trapezoid	

Use the words in the box below to fill in the names of the shapes.

| circle   quadrilateral   triangle   pentagon |

5. _____

6. _____

7. _____

8. _____

Trace copies of the plane shapes below.
Combine them to form the given shape.

— Example —

Trace 9 copies of the square below to form Shape A.

Use this shape	Shape A
9 ☐	

9.   Trace 8 copies of the triangle below to form Shape B.

Use this shape	Shape B
8 △	

10.   Trace 6 copies of the triangle below to form Shape C.

Use this shape	Shape C
△	⬡

11.   Trace 8 copies of the triangle below to form Shape D.

Use this shape	Shape D
◺	▭

12.   Trace 9 copies of the square below to form Shape E.

Use this shape	Shape E
▢	✚

Draw lines on each shape to show smaller shapes.

— **Example** —

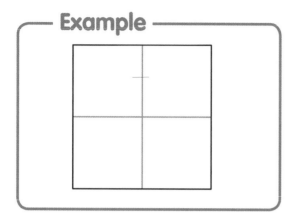

13.

14.

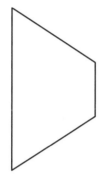

15.

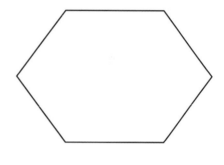

Draw lines on each figure to show how it is made with these shapes: triangle, square, rectangle, trapezoid, and hexagon. Not every shape is used each time.

— **Example** —

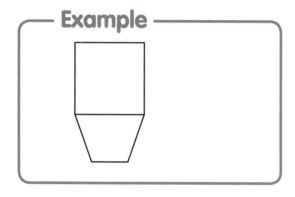

16.

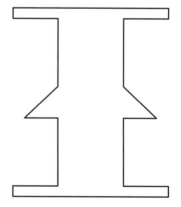

17.

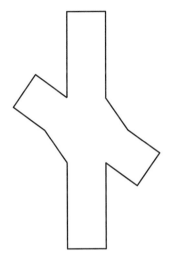

18.

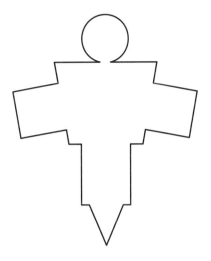

Copy each figure.

Example

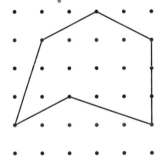 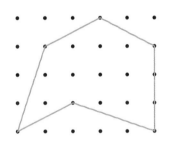

19.

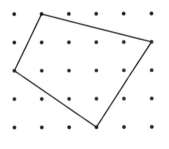

Copy each figure.

Example

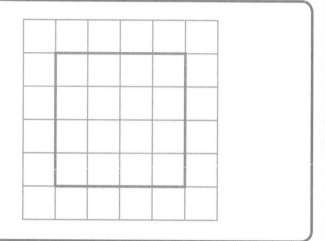

20.

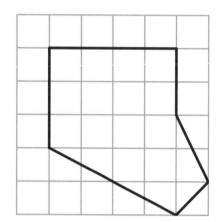   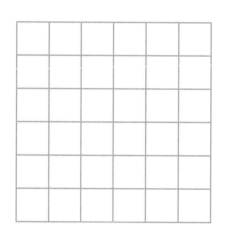

21.

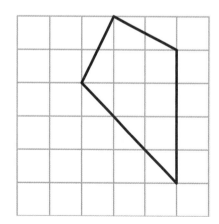

Worksheet 2 Solid Shapes

Look at the pictures.

Count and check (✔) the solid shapes that make up each picture.

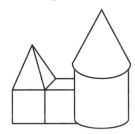

Example

Solid Shape	Check (✔)	Number
Rectangular prism		0
Cube	✔	2
Cone	✔	1
Cylinder	✔	1
Sphere		0
Pyramid	✔	1

1.

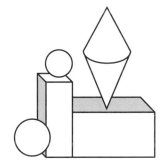

Solid Shape	Check (✔)	Number
Rectangular prism		
Cube		
Cone		
Cylinder		
Sphere		
Pyramid		

2.

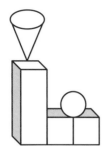

Solid Shape	Check (✔)	Number
Rectangular prism		
Cube		
Cone		
Cylinder		
Sphere		
Pyramid		

3.

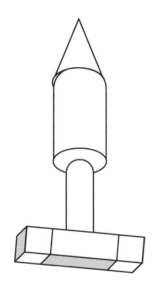

Solid Shape	Check (✔)	Number
Rectangular prism		
Cube		
Cone		
Cylinder		
Sphere		
Pyramid		

Write the number of faces on each shape.

4.

_____

5.

_____

6.

_____

7.

_____

Worksheet 3   Making Patterns

Look at the patterns.
Draw what comes next.

Example

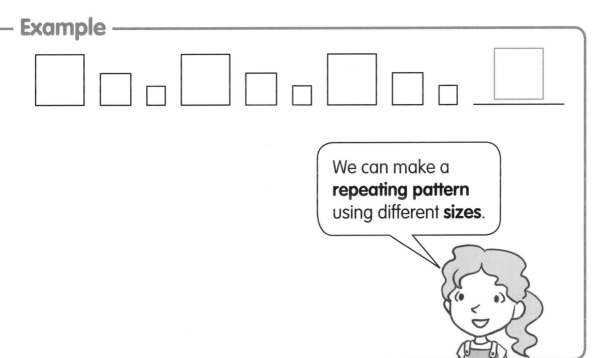

We can make a **repeating pattern** using different **sizes**.

1.

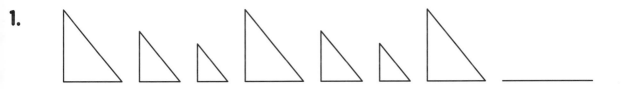

2.

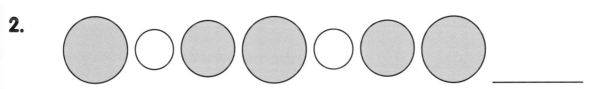

3.

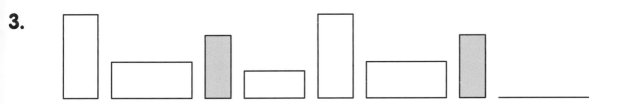

Draw the correct shapes to complete the pattern.

Example

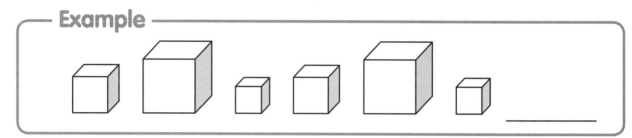

4.

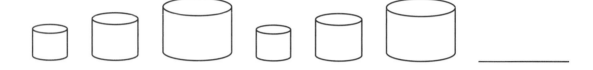

5.

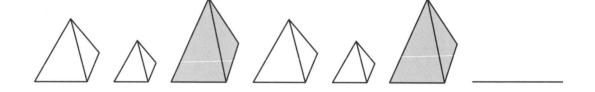

6.

What comes next?

Circle the correct shapes or figures to complete the pattern.

Example

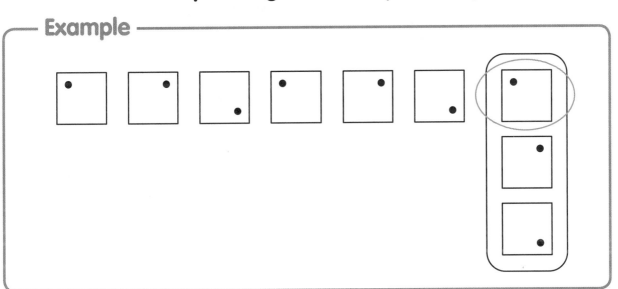

7.

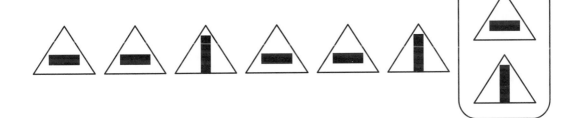

8.

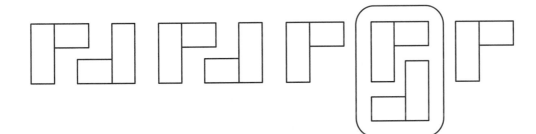

9.

Circle the correct shapes or figures to complete the pattern.

10.

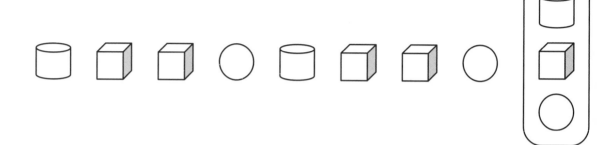

11.

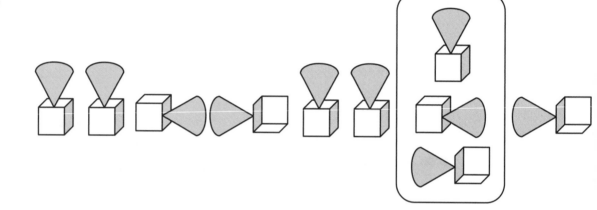

12.

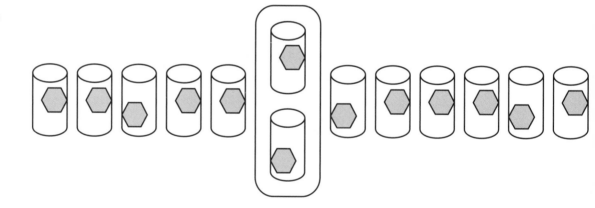

13.

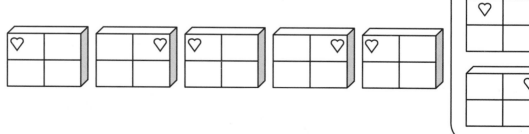

Answers

Chapter 10

Worksheet 1

1. Circle 77.
2. Circle 293.
3. Circle 268.
4. Circle 1,000.
5. $44 + 23 = \underline{67}$
6. $120 + 56 = \underline{176}$
7. $234 + 425 = 659$
   The sum is $\underline{659}$.
8. $178 + 258 = 436$
   The sum is $\underline{436}$.

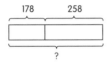

Worksheet 2

1. $7 + 2 = \underline{9}$; $10 + \underline{9} = \underline{19}$; So, $17 + 2 = \underline{19}$.
2. 15
3. $\underline{56} + 10 = \underline{66}$; $\underline{66} - 1 = \underline{65}$; So, $56 + 9 = \underline{65}$.
4. $\underline{3} + 4 = \underline{7}$; $140 + \underline{7} = \underline{147}$; So, $143 + 4 = \underline{147}$.
5. $256 + 10 = \underline{266}$; $\underline{266} - 3 = \underline{263}$; So, $256 + 7 = \underline{263}$
6. $10 + 10 = \underline{20}$; $\underline{20} + 1 = \underline{21}$; So, $11 + 10 = \underline{21}$.
7. 26
8. $20 + 30 = \underline{50}$; $\underline{304} + \underline{50} = \underline{354}$; So, $334 + 20 = \underline{354}$.
9. $232 + 100 = \underline{332}$; $\underline{332} - 40 = \underline{292}$; So, $232 + 60 = \underline{292}$.
10. $\underline{200} + 200 = \underline{400}$; $\underline{400} + 71 = \underline{471}$; So, $271 + 200 = \underline{471}$.

Worksheet 3

1. Circle 85.
2. Circle 153.
3. Circle 586.
4. Circle 204.
5. $85 - 73 = \underline{12}$
6. $76 - 45 = \underline{31}$
7. $57 - 34 = 23$
   The difference is $\underline{23}$.
8. $99 - 44 = 55$
   The difference is $\underline{55}$.

Worksheet 4

1. $7 - 6 = \underline{1}$; $30 + \underline{1} = \underline{31}$; So, $37 - 6 = \underline{31}$.
2. 25
3. $25 - 10 = \underline{15}$; $\underline{15} + 1 = \underline{16}$; So, $25 - 9 = \underline{16}$.
4. $6 - 2 = \underline{4}$; $\underline{130} + \underline{4} = \underline{134}$; So, $136 - 2 = \underline{134}$.

5. $256 - 10 = \underline{246}$; $\underline{246} + 2 = \underline{248}$; So, $256 - 8 = \underline{248}$.
6. $50 - 30 = \underline{20}$; $5 + \underline{20} = \underline{25}$; So, $55 - 30 = \underline{25}$.
7. 57
8. $\underline{40} - 30 = \underline{10}$; $102 + \underline{10} = \underline{112}$; So, $142 - 30 = \underline{112}$.
9. $\underline{182} - 100 = \underline{82}$; $\underline{82} + 40 = \underline{122}$; So, $182 - 60 = \underline{122}$.
10. $\underline{400} - 200 = \underline{200}$; $\underline{200} + 28 = \underline{228}$; So, $428 - 200 = \underline{228}$.

Worksheet 5

1. Estimate: $\underline{30}$
   Count: $\underline{32}$
2. 2; 6
3. 30; 60
4. 300; 400
5. Mark a cross on 31.
   Circle 30.
   30
6. Mark a cross on 72.
   Circle 70.
   70
7. Mark a cross on 76.
   Circle 80.
   80
8. Mark a cross on 49.
   Circle 50.
   50
9. Mark a cross on 113.
   Circle 110.
   110
10. Mark a cross on 661.
    Circle 660.
    660
11. Mark a cross on 597.
    Circle 600.
    600
12. Mark a cross on 915.
    Circle 920.
    920
13. 232 is about $\underline{230}$.
    556 is about $\underline{560}$.
    $232 + 556$ is about $\underline{790}$.
    Because $\underline{790}$ is close to 788, the answer is reasonable.
14. $158 + 265 = \underline{423}$
    Check: $\underline{160} + \underline{270} = \underline{430}$
15. $355 + 147 = \underline{502}$
    Check: $\underline{360} + \underline{150} = \underline{510}$
16. 439 is about $\underline{440}$.
    127 is about $\underline{130}$.
    $439 - 127$ is about $\underline{310}$.
    Because $\underline{310}$ is close to 312, the answer is reasonable.

17. 658 − 232 = <u>426</u>
 Check: <u>660</u> − <u>230</u> = <u>430</u>
18. 529 − 214 = <u>315</u>
 Check: <u>530</u> − <u>210</u> = <u>320</u>
19. 152 + 89 = <u>241</u>
 152 is about <u>150</u>.
 89 is about <u>90</u>.
 152 + 89 is about <u>150</u> + <u>90</u>.
 Yes, the answer is reasonable.
20. 558 − 312 = <u>246</u>
 558 is about <u>560</u>.
 312 is about <u>310</u>.
 558 − 312 is about <u>560</u> − <u>310</u>.
 Yes, the answer is reasonable.

Chapter 11

Worksheet 1

1. <u>1¢</u>
2. <u>25¢</u>
3. <u>10¢</u>
4. <u>5¢</u>
5. Answers vary.
 Sample:
 Circle 3 dimes, 1 quarter, and 2 nickels.
6. Answers vary.
 Sample:
 Circle 2 quarters, and 3 dimes.
7. Color the $1 bills blue, the $5 bills green, the $10 bills yellow, and the $20 bills red.
8. <u>5</u> $1 bills
9. <u>2</u> $5 bills
10. <u>3</u> $10 bills
11. <u>2</u> $20 bills
12. $<u>5</u>
13. $<u>10</u>
14. ten-dollar
15. The chapter book costs $<u>6</u>.
16. The sweater costs $<u>21</u>.
17. dimes
18. Circle 2 quarters and 5 dimes.
19. Circle 7 dimes, 5 nickels, and 5 pennies.
20. equal to
21. more than
22. less than
23. Hillary has <u>5</u> dollars and <u>25</u> cents.
 Hillary has $<u>5.25</u>.
24. $20; $20.00

25. $22; $22.00
26. 31¢; $0.31
27. 46¢; $0.46
28. 1 dollar; 25 cents; $1.25
29. 20 dollars; 60 cents; $20.60
30. $0.27
31. $3.15
32. $10
33. 90¢
34. 565¢
35. 1095¢

Worksheet 2

1. Mike
2. Audrey

Worksheet 3

1. $458 − $13 = $445
 Mrs. Garcia has $<u>445</u> in all.
 $445 − $123 = $322
 Mrs. Garcia has $<u>322</u> left.
2. $3 + $1 + $2 = $6
 She paid $<u>6</u> in all.
3.

$16	$12	$10

 ?

 $16 + $12 + $10 = $38
 Kelly had $<u>38</u> at first.
4.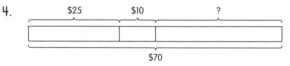

 $70 − $25 − $10 = $35
 Tristan had $<u>35</u> left.
5. 5 nickels = 25¢
 4 dimes = 40¢
 25¢ + 40¢ = 65¢ or $0.65
 She has collected <u>65¢</u>.
6. $7.45 − $0.80 = $6.65
 Mrs. Powell has $<u>6.65</u>.

7. 2 nickels = 10¢
5 pennies = 5¢
3 dollar bills = $3
$3.00 + $0.10 + $0.05 = $3.15
$3.15 − $1.35 = $1.80
Janet had $1.80 left.

8. Bread cost $2.35
$2.35 + $2.10 = $4.45
Jill had $4.45 at first.

Chapter 12

Worksheet 1

1. A, C, and D; B, E

2. [✗]

3. [ ]

4. [✗]

5.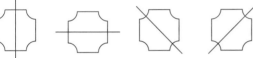

6.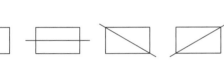

7.

One-third

8.

One-quarter

9.
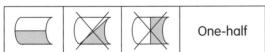
One-half

10. $\frac{1}{2}$

11. $\frac{1}{4}$

12. $\frac{1}{2}$

13. $\frac{1}{3}$

14. $\frac{1}{4}$

Worksheet 2

1. $\frac{1}{3}; \frac{1}{2}$

$\frac{1}{2}$ is greater than $\frac{1}{3}$.

$\frac{1}{3}$ is less than $\frac{1}{2}$.

2. $\frac{1}{4}; \frac{1}{3}$

$\frac{1}{3}$ is greater than $\frac{1}{4}$.

$\frac{1}{4}$ is less than $\frac{1}{3}$.

3. $\frac{1}{4}$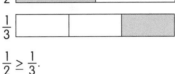

$\frac{1}{2}$

$\frac{1}{4} \leq \frac{1}{2}$

4. $\frac{1}{2}$

$\frac{1}{3}$

$\frac{1}{2} \geq \frac{1}{3}$.

Worksheet 3

1.

2.

3.

4. $\frac{2}{4}$ or $\frac{1}{2}$

5. $\frac{1}{2}$

6. $\frac{2}{3}$

7. Circle $\frac{1}{2}$ and $\frac{2}{2}$.

8. Circle $\frac{1}{3}$ and $\frac{3}{3}$.

9. Circle $\frac{4}{4}$ and $\frac{2}{4}$.

10. Circle $\frac{2}{3}$ and $\frac{3}{3}$.

11.

12. $\frac{3}{3}$ or 1

13. $\frac{2}{4}$ or $\frac{1}{2}$

14. $\frac{3}{4}$

15. $\frac{3}{4}$

16. $\frac{2}{3}$

17.

18. $\frac{1}{3}$

19. $\frac{2}{4}$ or $\frac{1}{2}$

20. $\frac{1}{2}$

Chapter 13

Worksheet 1

1. more
2. more
3. less
4. less
5. less
6. less
7. more
8. 2
9. 5

Worksheet 2

1. taller
2. Longest: Tricycle B

Shortest: Tricycle C

3. Tallest: Tree C

Shortest: Tree B

4. A; 3
5. Q; 3
6. Patricia; 1

Worksheet 3

1. 6
2. 2
3. 6
4. 4
5. 7
6. Draw a part of a line B that is 2 inches long.
7. Draw a part of a line C that is 4 inches long.
8. Draw a part of a line D that is 3 inches long.
9. 2
10. 8
11. 7

Worksheet 4

1. C
2. Flag Pole A is 6 inches long.
   Flag Pole B is 9 inches long.
   9 – 6 = 3
   Flag Pole B is 3 inches taller than Flag Pole A.
3. Marker A is 4 inches long.
   Marker B is 6 inches long.
   6 – 4 = 2
   Marker B is 2 inches longer than Marker A.
4. Answers vary.
   Sample:
   length of my desk
5. Answers vary.

Worksheet 5

1. 420 + 230 = 650
   Gillian cycled 650 feet in all.
2. 69 + 164 = 233
   The total length of the 2 walking paths was 233 feet.
3. 78 – 45 = 33
   The other piece of string is 33 inches long.
4. 70 – 23 = 47
   Dion's brother is 47 inches tall.
5. 62 + 12 = 74
   Antonio's sister is 74 inches tall.

6.

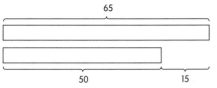

65

50   15

65 − 15 = 50

Victoria's sister is <u>50</u> inches tall.

7.

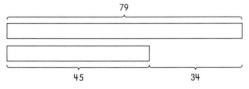

79

45   34

a. 45 + 34 = 79

   Rope B is <u>79</u> inches long.

b. 79 + 45 = 124

   Rope A and B are <u>124</u> inches long in all.

8.

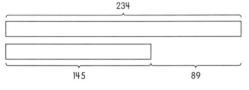

234

145   89

a. 145 + 89 = 234

   Train B is <u>234</u> ft long.

b. 234 + 145 = 379

   The total length of both trains is <u>379</u> feet.

Chapter 14

Worksheet 1

1.   1
2.   7
3.   10
4.   25

5.

6.

Worksheet 2

1.   5:05
2.   Circle 4:20.
3.   Circle 2:35.
4.   35 minutes after 4 or four thirty-five
5.   15 minutes after 7 or seven fifteen
6.

7.

8.

9.

10.

11.

12.

13.

14.

15.

16.

17.

18.   35 minutes after 12 or twelve thirty-five

19.   55 minutes after 7 or seven fifty-five

Worksheet 3

1. P.M.   2. A.M.
3. P.M.   4. 4.15 P.M.
5. 8:40 P.M.   6. 10.15 A.M.
7. 10:15 A.M., 4:15 P.M., 8:40 P.M.
        earliest

Worksheet 4

1. 1 hour   2. 1:00 P.M.
3. 30 minutes   4. 3:30 P.M.

Chapter 15

Worksheet 1

1. 6
2. 15
3. 30
4. 30; There are 30 stickers in all.
5. 3, 6, 9
   3 × 3 = 9
   Valencia has 9 tulips in all.
6. 8 × 3 = 24
   There are 24 photos in all.

Worksheet 2

1. 6 × 2 = 12
   The hens have 12 legs in all.
2. 3 × 3 = 9
   Jon ties 9 balloons in all.
3. 9 × 3 = 27
   Susan has 27 plums in all.
4. 2; 12
5. 4; 16
6. 6; 21
7. 3; 27
8. 21; 21

Worksheet 3

1. 8
2. 20
3. 40
4. 20; Tara pays $20 for the 5 party hats.
5. 4, 8, 12, 16, 20, 24, 28
   7 × 4 = 28
   She jogs 28 miles in a week.
6. 8 × 4 = 32
   The rabbits have 32 legs in all.

Worksheet 4

1. 2 × 5 = 10
   Mina uses 10 cubes of ice.
2. 7 × $4 = $28
   Kelsey pays $28 in all.
3. 9 × 4 = 36
   Eileen baked 36 muffins in all.
4. 2; 8
5. 2; 18
6. 8; 28
7. 4; 36
8. 32; 32

Worksheet 5

1. 10 ÷ 2 = 5
   5 forks are in each group.
2. 7; 7
3. 10; 10   4. 4; 4
5. $20 ÷ 5 = $4
   Each child gets $4.
6. 8 ÷ 4 = 2
   There are 2 shelves.
7. 30 ÷ 10 = 3
   Donna picks 3 peaches from each tree.

Chapter 16

Worksheet 1

1. 12   2. 15
3. 36   4. 40
5. 70   6. 12; 12
7. 16; 16

Worksheet 2

1. 7   2. 5
3. 5   4. 9
5. 8   6. 5; 5
7. 8; 8   8. 8; 8
9. 4; 4

Worksheet 3

1. 16; 16   2. 5; 5
3. 12; 12   4. 5; 5
5. 12; 12   6. 6; 6
7. 28; 28   8. 3; 3

Chapter 17

Worksheet 1

1. 4	2. 2
3. 4	4. 19
5. 6	6. 12
7. 10	8. 25
9. 35	10. 18
11. 9	12. 6
13. 18	14. 12
15. bowls; cups	16. plates
17. 12	18. 2
19. 12	20. jog; skate
21. dance	22. 6
23. 4	24. 9

Worksheet 2

1.

Animal	Tally	Number of Animals
Duck	﹣HHT	5
Turtle	﹣HHT ////	9
Dragonfly	﹣HHT ﹣HHT //	12
Flamingo	////	4

2. ○○
3. ○○○○○○○
4. △△△
5. △△△△
6. △△△△△△△

7.

Fruit	Tally	Pieces of Fruit
Orange	////	4
Apple	﹣HHT ﹣HHT //	12
Peach	﹣HHT ///	8
Pear	﹣HHT /	6

8.

Key: Each ⬭ stands for 2 pieces of fruit.

9.

Sport	Tally	Number of Children
Baseball	﹣HHT ﹣HHT ﹣HHT	15
Basketball	﹣HHT ﹣HHT //	12
Soccer	﹣HHT ////	9
Tennis	﹣HHT /	6

10. **Title:** <u>Favorite Sport</u>

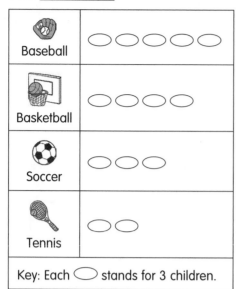

Baseball	⬭ ⬭ ⬭ ⬭ ⬭
Basketball	⬭ ⬭ ⬭ ⬭
Soccer	⬭ ⬭ ⬭
Tennis	⬭ ⬭

Key: Each ⬭ stands for 3 children.

Worksheet 3

1. 18
2. Lenard; Sandy
3. 6
4. 45
5. 3
6. 3
7. 32
8. 14
9. B; C
10. A; E; 8
11. 6

12. **Title:** <u>Favorite Color</u>

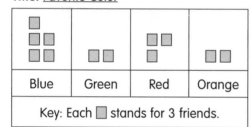

Blue	Green	Red	Orange
◻◻◻◻◻	◻◻	◻◻◻	◻◻

Key: Each ◻ stands for 3 friends.

13. 2
14. 9

Worksheet 4

1.

Month	Number of Students
January	2
February	2
March	3
April	4
May	1

2.

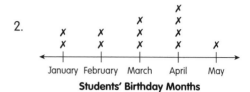

Students' Birthday Months

3. 12
4. April
5. May
6. March
7.

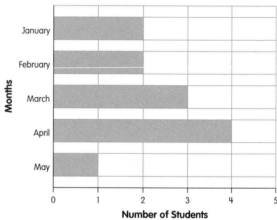

Months of Students' Birthdays

Chapter 18

Worksheet 1

1. a. B and D   b. A and C
2. 5; 8   3. 3; 5

Worksheet 2

1. baseball and watermelon
2. Answers vary.
   Sample:
   refrigerator and kitchen counter
3. Answers vary.
   Sample:
   toilet rolls and light bulbs
4. Circle cube and cylinder.
5. Circle cone and sphere.

Chapter 19

Worksheet 1

1.

Plane Shape	Check (✓)	Number
Triangle	✓	2
Square		0
Rectangle	✓	5
Circle	✓	3

2.

Plane Shape	Check (✓)	Number
Triangle		0
Square	✓	4
Rectangle	✓	3
Circle	✓	2

3.

Plane Shape	Number
Triangle	3
Square	3
Rectangle	5
Circle	1
Hexagon	1
Trapezoid	6

4.

Plane Shape	Number
Triangle	2
Square	1
Rectangle	9
Circle	2
Hexagon	4
Trapezoid	0

5. quadrilateral
6. circle
7. pentagon
8. triangle

9.   10.

11.   12.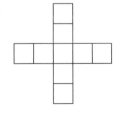

Answers vary for Exercises 13 to 18.
Sample:

13.    14.

15. 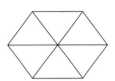   16.

17. 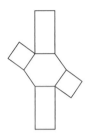   18.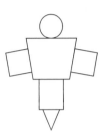

19.   20.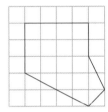

21.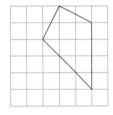

Worksheet 2

1.

Solid Shape	Check (✓)	Number
Rectangular prism	✓	2
Cube		0
Cone	✓	2
Cylinder		0
Sphere	✓	2
Pyramid		0

2.

Solid Shape	Check (✓)	Number
Rectangular prism	✓	1
Cube	✓	2
Cone	✓	1
Cylinder		0
Sphere	✓	1
Pyramid		0

3.

Solid Shape	Check (✓)	Number
Rectangular prism	✓	1
Cube	✓	2
Cone	✓	1
Cylinder	✓	2
Sphere		0
Pyramid		0

4. 6

5. 2

6. 5

7. 6

Worksheet 3

1.

2.

3.

4.

5.

6.

7.

8.

9.

10.

11.

12.

13.